S0-BRS-601

616.85
R74r

78234

DATE DUE			
Apr 15 74			
Apr 12 75			
May 9 73 78			
Mar 6 75			
Oct 7 7 8			

WITHDRAWN

THE RIDDLE

OF

CRUELTY

THE RIDDLE
OF
CRUELTY

by

G. Rothman, M. D.

PHILOSOPHICAL LIBRARY

New York

CARL A. RUDISILL LIBRARY
LENOIR RHYNE COLLEGE

©Copyright, 1971, by Philosophical Library, Inc.

15 East 40 Street, New York, N. Y. 10016

All rights reserved

Library of Congress Catalog Card No. 74-118310
SBN 8022-2345-1

616.85
R74r
78234
Mar 1972

Manufactured in the United States of America

A WORD TO THE READER

It is with deep satisfaction that I introduce Dr. Rothman's intriguing book. During discussions concerning the character structure of modern man and the problems of interaction between psychological and sociological factors which took place in Freud's summerhouse on the Semmering mountains, Freud discovered Dr. Rothman's creative mind, empathy, and unusual intuition which predestine one for psychoanalytic practice. He arranged for Dr. Rothman's training with me and Dr. Bernfeld—later president of the San Francisco Psychoanalytic Institute.

From experience of many years of psychiatric work Dr. Rothman demonstrates in this book how sadomasochistic trends develop and how they can be modified and cured; hundreds of reports and data have been gathered with scrupulous care and are quoted throughout the text to give the reader timely, useful information on the subject of cruelty. Professional and laymen will appreciate that this popular and instructive book is written in nontechnical language, and that it does not start with lengthy theoretical explanations but takes us right into medias res.

THEODOR REIK

1968

TABLE OF CONTENTS

THE RIDDLE

OF

CRUELTY

CASE HISTORY: example of sado-masochism caused by incestuous activities.

On the observation ward two strong attendants were holding a young girl down on her bed. She was screaming and trying to fight. "You can't give me my treatments, doctor!" She yelled, "Go away, you are much too small." The doctor, motioning the attendants out of the room, sat down at Millie's bedside, stroking her softly. This had a soothing effect and she gradually calmed down. Although she looked like a teenager she was in her early twenties. She was pale, had short light-blonde hair and a slight body build. "My boss turned me in," she said. "I was hoping he would give me my treatment, but he refused." Pulling down her hospital gown, she pointed to bites on her neck and scars and bruises on her arms and chest. Gradually a contact was established between Millie and the doctor and the picture was clarified:

She had been so unhappy all these years; there seemed to be no way out. She had made everybody else unhappy too. She had driven her father into suicide, killed her grandmother, and destroyed her mother's second marriage. Could all these self-accusations really be justified?

The mother appeared, dressed in black, crying, and imploring the doctor to help them. She amplified the history her daughter had given. Millie's father, a government-employed engineer and surveyor, was frequently stationed in distant places and therefore absent from home for long periods of time. The mother found consolation in religious and social activities. She was rather frigid. However, the parental relationship became somewhat closer after the long-awaited child was born.

Millie was very proud to be selected for a role in the

1

Christmas play. Millie and her mother were greatly dismayed when the father, who objected strongly to religious activities, came to church and took Millie home just as she was about to go on stage. The mother continued to devote most of her time and energy to religious activities and often came home but late in the evening. Because of the lack of home-life the marriage deteriorated and there were frequent arguments. Coming home late one evening after a church dinner she found the little girl still awake. The husband was in bed reading the newspaper. She noticed that the bedclothes were in a state of disarray. He reassured her that everything was alright.

One morning while mother and daughter were playing together, Millie complained, "Daddy didn't give me the little dollie he has already promised me so often." "Maybe you will get it as a Birthday-present. You'll be seven next month," replied the mother. "Oh no," said Millie, "he promised to give it to me every time if I was good to our pet." "But we don't have a pet," said the mother. "Yes, our snake," replied Millie, "don't you know Daddy has a snake? It has a mouth but no eyes. It's very cute. I have to stroke it and caress it and kiss its head. Then Daddy goes into the cupboard and when he comes out again the snake is gone. I went into the cupboard after him, but I could never find it again. Daddy always says if I am good to the snake and caress it he will give me the dolly next time, but whenever I ask for it, he says he hasn't bought it yet."

When the father came home in the late afternoon the mother asked him whether he had promised Millie a little doll. The father confirmed it; but when the mother asked him about the snake, he became very angry. He tried to seize Millie, yelling, "you little rattle-snake! I'll give it to you!" The mother, having experienced her husband's violent temper before, called to Millie, "run downstairs to the neighbors!" Thereupon the husband threw himself on his wife, knocking her to the floor. When blood gushed from her head he poured whiskey down her throat, placed the bottle beside her on the floor, called the ambulance and said: "My wife is an alcoholic. She fell down while she was drunk and must have hurt herself. She

2

is bleeding." The wife was taken to a hospital, where she had to stay several weeks.

Later, when Millie came back from the neighbors she was beaten mercilessly by her father, who threatened to kill her. She was so terrified that she did not even feel the pain, submitting completely to the punishment, which she felt she had deserved for telling the mother about the forbidden tender activities.

When the mother returned from the hospital Millie's behaviour had changed completely: Formerly a vivacious, friendly, little girl, she was now quiet and withdrawn, did not want to play anymore, and sat in a corner all by herself. The relationship between husband and wife had also changed; it was cool and distant; the husband arranged to be transferred to another city. A few weeks later the mother was informed that he had committed suicide. She told the child, "Daddy was killed in a car accident." However, Millie overheard telephone conversations and knew the truth. She felt she had caused her father's death. She lost speech and tactile sense and saw skulls in the pattern of the wallpaper. Having hated her father and wished for his death, she was overwhelmed by guilt feelings when her wish was gratified. She enacted death herself by becoming catatonic and had to be taken to a hospital. When the mother visited her and acted so concerned, Millie felt her mother still loved and needed her; whereupon her health improved. She returned to school and being of good intelligence she was able not only to keep up but even excelled. However, she could not play with the other children and was introverted. She felt different, yet longed for a close contact with another human being, which she was unable to establish. She asked a boy in her class to beat her, but he looked at her in amazement—he did not understand. During the age of puberty she felt even more lonely. Psychotherapy was suggested at that time by the school nurse, but the child could not relate to anybody and therapy was given up after a few sessions, since both mother and the child were reluctant to uncover the traumatic experiences and the mother even hoped the child would eventually forget them.

3

The atmosphere at home was somewhat gloomy until the mother finally remarried. The stepfather was kind but distant. Millie, initially indifferent towards him, began to display coquettish, seductive behaviour. He had been completely informed by the mother of the occurrences during her first marriage. Therefore, he met Millie's attempts at seduction with indifference. Millie, feeling rejected, longing to get him out of his cool indifference, and wanting to be as important to him as she had been to her real father, eventually undressed in front of him. When admonished in a friendly but cool manner to get dressed, she requested to be beaten. When he did not comply despite her repeated attempts, she felt desperate. She longed to be in the hands of somebody who would have complete power over her life and death. She wanted to be able to incite her stepfather to such a rage that he would be beyond himself and treat her as her father had treated her. When she did not succeed, she went to her grandmother, telling a phantasied story, and complaining that the stepfather had seduced her. The grandmother, completely horrified, questioned the stepfather. Thereupon the stepfather lost his patience and actually beat her. Soon afterwards the grandmother died, probably of old age. Millie felt as if she had caused her death.

Gradually the relationship between mother and stepfather deteriorated. When they were divorced, Millie again felt guilty, imagining that she had caused her father's and grandmother's death, and her mother's divorce. Henceforth she was obsessed by the desire to be beaten.

Since she had developed into an attractive girl, she readily caught the attention of boys. However, she was completely disinterested in them. She wanted a man much older than herself, longing for the excitement she had experienced at the hands of her father. Eventually she met an older gentleman, who wanted to marry her. But when she asked to be beaten, he couldn't bring himself to seriously hurt her and slapped her but slightly. She became disinterested in him and finally paid complete strangers to beat her. On one such occasion she was beaten and subsequently taken sexually by three men jointly. On another occasion she paid a Negro to bite her to such an extent that she was left with permanent scars. Eventually she tried to seduce her boss into beating her. When he saw the marks on her neck and arms, he became apprehensive of being drawn into some kind of unpleasantness and therefore arranged that she be taken to the hospital. Resisting psychotherapy, she tried to seduce a male therapist into beating her. She was almost obsessed by the craving for at ntion, wanting to transport her partner—a father substitute—. 'o such a highly emotional state that he would be beyond h. iself. It gave her a feeling of power to get him so excited that he lost control. She wandered around the ward at night, seducing male attendants. She was transferred to a female therapist.

During the ensuing psychotherapy sessions she described that she was always looking for new love-objects. Nobody could satisfy her for any length of time. When she found a new love object it tore her out of her depression but for a short while. Because she had been so deprived in her childhood she still depended too much on others. During this stage of development guilt feelings had been instilled into her. Therefore her conscience demanded punishment and retaliation. Usually she was depressed and defensive. When she could not obtain the desired reaction from her partner she felt rage and hatred.

Working through her traumatic experiences in psychotherapy, she remembered that she was in the depths of despair when her mother came home from the hospital: The mother was no longer the kind, dedicated, considerate and warmhearted person, she had been before; although she forced herself to be tender, it was no longer natural sincere affection. But then, when *Millie* was in the hospital, the mother showed genuine love and concern. Millie now repeated her childhood pattern: Only through misery could she win love. Thus she defeated herself in school, in her job, and even in therapy when she was close to success. She wanted to atone for having destroyed both her mother's marriages. The prevailing depressive feeling was one of powerlessness and helplessness. She enjoyed not only the feeling of helplessness, which she had experienced when completely in the power of the punishing father but also the feeling of power she had when she transported her father—or now her partners—into a state of such high excitement. As long as she was made to submit by force, she need not feel responsible for taking away her mother's men. She could not possibly experience orgasm or any desire for ordinary sexual intercourse. She remained the eternal child—wanting lust without guilt, without responsibility. Since it was the father, who seduced her, she need not feel guilty; she just had to submit to the strong father. She also wanted to be a better wife to him than her old frigid mother. She hated the mother when she had the father all to herself, and she hated the father when by sending his wife to the hospital he had deprived her of her mother. Ruthlessly she knew how to achieve what she wanted, even utilizing her grandmother, when falsely accusing the stepfather. Daydreaming drove her into splendid isolation. In vain did she try to free herself from this castrating relationship with her parents; she could not fall in love with anyone and was frigid like her mother. In order not to see, not to be aware, she tried to calm her guilt by taking drugs. Her favorite drug was atropine, because through its effect of initial excitement followed by apathy she was able to reexperience the emotional state of her childhood.

It is characteristic of masochists that they feel their strength in being helpless, docile, and submissive. Through defeat they dominate their partner. This was carried to the extreme in Millie's case. By accepting punishment willingly, she won the love of her parent. Masochists often provoke being hurt; Millie even threatened to commit suicide. Had she carried out her threat she would have been able to punish her mother and make her feel guilty. When telling her mother the first time about the dolly, she somehow arranged to be hurt, being hit by the father. She repeatedly said: "He gave me love, he made me feel that I was so important to him." In her desire to dominate, she showed a revengeful attitude towards men: they were humiliated by being paid for their services and although entering into activities of great intimacy they were not supposed to have sexual intercourse with her. Had her guilt not led to masochism she might have become a criminal. This case shows that masochism is not just a state of passive suffering but reversed sadism.

The case of Millie is not unique, but serves to illustrate a problem which is more common than we may think. In the following chapters we shall attempt to gain a better understanding of the riddle in the relationship of cruelty to pleasure.

INTRODUCTION: active and passive cruelty; cruel rulers in olden times.

Throughout the history of mankind certain trends are prevalent during given periods of development: In ancient times man was busy discovering and mastering the world a r o u n d him. He had to provide food and shelter, and was preoccupied investigating and subduing the forces of nature, such as fire, water, and electricity. His energies were taken up with inventing tools and machines. When the outside world was under better control he began to look into himself, trying to find out what was going on within himself.

Since heaven has gained widened proportions with the development of space-exploration, modern man is no longer satisfied with the customary explanations and concepts such as the "workshop of nature." In surgery organ transplant has led to new questions being raised as to whether the mind be just an emanation of the brain and the soul be nonexistent. Pharmacology and psychology have contributed to the investigation and clarification of established concepts such as soul, mind, instincts, morality and ethics. Man stops to hark into himself and to ask — "why?"

Actions formerly judged with approval or condemnation by religion and court, are now critically explored and investigated for their motivation. Our sexual life is no longer hushed over and shrouded in mystery; we try to understand. We realize that the clarification of sexual problems leads to the unwinding and clarifying of social, political, and legal problems as well.

Gratification derived from exerting cruelty is deeply ingrained in nature: observation of animals and human beings alike shows that already small puppies fight and hurt each other playfully, and human children do not act any differently. They enjoy their growing strength and prove it by fighting

8

with each other. Man is constitutionally endowed with a certain quantity of aggression—aggressive drives are natural and normal. Ontogeny recapitulates phylogeny; in the realm of behaviour no less than in the growth of the physical embryo.

Gratification derived from submitting to cruelty is not as apparent as pleasure derived from exerting cruelty. Although we can trace both kinds—active and passive cruelty—through history the manifestation of active cruelty is much more evident.

The most intricate contraptions have been constructed to satisfy the desire for cruelty. We are horrified to read in our history books about Tiberius, Nero, Calligula and Theodora persecuting and tormenting their victims; Tiberius was called by his contemporaries a lump of clay mixed with blood. He retreated upon the island of Capri in the Gulf of Naples, exclusively dedicating himself to slowly tormenting and killing people. Victims were required by him daily, and he wallowed in their sufferings and deaths. Roman citizens, having incurred animosity, and expecting to come before a court, are said to have preferred suicide to such torture. Tiberius said of such people, who committed suicide,—"he escaped me."

It makes us shudder to read descriptions of evil deeds such as Nero committed, e.g. making the city of Rome go up in flames in order to enjoy the sight, or killing his mistress with a kick of his foot, or igniting human beings whose clothes had been drenched in flammable liquids in order to use them as torches. However, expressions of cruelty are not only found in ancient times. In every period of history we find individuals in whose character make-up cruelty is predominant. Often it is an increased drive for aggression which spurs them on to attain power and influence. Montesquieu, in his "De l'Esprit des Lois" explained that persons in power are inclined to misuse it, going farther and farther, until they find some restraint or obstacle. This is confirmed throughout history. Poets and sculptors have seen to it that the terrible deeds of cruel rulers such as Alexander Borgia and his son, or Ivan the Terrible and Phillip II are not forgotten and that such crowned criminals enjoy sad immortality.

Courts have tried to restrict asocial drives by enforcing law, but human nature has not changed. In vain do clergymen preach that these aberrations no longer belong in our "enlightened times" and that man should not degrade himself to the level of animals. Still nowadays human beings torment each other in every conceivable way, and injustice and cruelty still reign in our modern society. We need not even attend court proceedings or read handbooks of legal medicine. Our daily newspapers are full of manifestations of cruelty, which still appeals to the masses as it did in ancient times. Newspaper circulation is increased when some cruel act, such as murder, appears on the front page.

We need not go into descriptions of horrors from concentration camps; right in our midst children are often tormented and killed. This has become so widespread that a standard diagnosis in general hospitals is "Battered Child Syndrome." Another favorite topic in our daily news is "married partners" driven on by jealousy, mutilating and killing each other. Apparently our pride in our so-called "Age of Humanity" is hardly justified.

What we know and clearly understand can no longer overpower us and get out of control; therefore every contribution to the investigation of manifestations of cruelty from the point of view of history, philosophy, sociology, medicine, and psychology may contribute towards enlightenment and decrease cruelty.

Violence is the assertion of aggressive force; as long as it is aim-directed it is normal and in a way necessary for certain activities (construction, surgery). Only when it is not aim directed and not controlled is it destructive.

INVESTIGATION BY PHILOSOPHY: identification with the aggressor; compassion, empathy, pretense.

Philosophy contains a number of systems which even glorify cruelty. The most conspicuous one in our time—Nazism—goes back to the teachings of Nietzsche (2, 3). His bloodthirsty theories of the "Superman" led psychologists to conclude that his sex-life was abnormal. This is confirmed by his family history: his father died when he was still a small child; being exposed to predominantly maternal influence—which was reenforced by a domineering sister—led him to overvalue male character-components. He is said to have had an intimate relationship with his sister, with whom he lived until he was hospitalized with manifest schizophrenia. His "Superman" had to break with all tradition, his principal goal being to satisfy his drives, his desire for power, regardless of custom. Compassion was supposed to be the virtue of the weak, who were expected to serve the strong.

Schopenhauer had been afflicted with syphilis in his early manhood. Consequently he came to hate all women and became homosexual. Some philosophers postulate that cruelty is intensified by witnessing cruel actions. However, to be impressed by it positively the drive for cruelty must in inborn. Schopenhauer believed that a cruel person enjoys his own power and superiority. This can not entirely be confirmed because even when people are being tormented upon the instigation of a third person, the cruel individual enjoys it: The Romans applauded upon witnessing gladiators being torn apart, which was commanded by the emperor. We can assume that the people could not possibly have experienced a feeling of power. They even must have felt faint, having to consider the possibility that they themselves might be in the gladiator's place the very next day. They enjoyed identification with the aggressor just be-

11

cause they had little—or no—possibility to exert power and/or cruelty in their daily life.

Furthermore, one's own feeling of helplessness, misery, and inferiority is relieved when seeing others suffering more. Beggars know that from experience: They often exaggerate their disabilities in order to receive more alms. People looking at their suffering feel that in comparison their own misery is minimal. Often they even experience a feeling of guilt and apprehension that something similar might happen to them; the fear of what might happen, if they lost all their possessions, even their health, engenders a feeling of guilt. Compassion is not always genuine empathy—sharing, but a mixture of fear and compensated inferiority-feeling, leading to voluntary sacrifice. A well-known prostitute attracted attention recently: She pretended to be blind. Being young and pretty, she attracted many customers, most of them elderly men, who were gratified to assume the role of a good father and protector, especially when she told them a sentimental tale—that her mother was dead and her father had left her, and she had nobody to take care of her. Her companion, a middle-aged beggar, used to sit cross-legged, covered with a carpet, giving the impression that his legs were amputated below the knee. He used to tremble and shake periodically. He came to the attention of policemen when they noticed him elegantly dressed and walking briskly.

People identify with both—the aggressor and the victim. Slaves, in order to escape their feeling of powerlessness, took on as their own the will of their master. Such identification with the enemy was observed in concentration camps. Eisler (4) explains that people are inclined to have a feeling of contempt and scorn for those, who are humiliated and have to submit to physical punishment, suffering and torture. This stands in sharp contrast to ethical sentiments that have become rooted in us by tradition.

In order to understand such an apparent contradiction we have to observe the development of our conscience—superego. Hoppe (5) describes that observing children we find that wish fulfillment and magical thinking, together with feelings of

12

omnipotence, tend to appear in the second year of life. Compliance and identification with the aggressor represent the primordia of conscience. Some concentration-camp inmates regressed to the earliest phase of compliance. The Camp-guards were elevated to parental images with which they would identify and which they would even imitate. The persecuted people, deprived of any narcissism, eventually felt that perhaps the persecutors were right. Revenge, anger, rage and hostility against the persecutor were repressed. They were ashamed and felt guilty. They completely identified with the enemy, as is characteristic of masochism. The masochist longs for situations in which any resistance is made impossible. The more humiliating the situation, the greater the enjoyment. Through masochistic identification one can become the powerful and loved enemy. Bak (6) describes how a boy, who was unjustly and cruelly punished by his father throughout his childhood, eventually came to admire him and longing to be accepted and loved, he identified with his father. Through masochistic identification he became the father. This led to sublimated homosexuality and eventually to masochism.

In some cases the ego protects itself against the masochistic threat by detachment from the admired person, eventually hating him. Sadistic phantasies appear if the ego can no longer master the hatred; it may come to sadistic actions. The outcome may be flight, megalomania, murder, suicide, or simply depression. Depressions are often self-accusations and punishment for sadistic phantasies. All depressed people hate.

Some individuals, suppressed and subjugated for long periods of time, react to traumatic experiences with aggression, e.g. the Negroes. Since aggression and hatred become their main device for coping with unpleasant or difficult situations, they suffer from a kind of chronic hate-addiction. At first directed towards the enemy, such hatred often spreads to include the whole world that has permitted such cruelty. Nietzsche stated that to be alone with one's conscience is terrifying. A severe and punitive conscience diminishes one's ego-strength and self-evaluation. which may lead to depersonalization—one may lose one's identity. In such a case self-destructive tendencies emerge. Hatred may mobilize guilt feelings; they may be turned against the Self and lead to somatic diseases and self-destruction, or towards vegetating in apathy and hopelessness.

Usually, the less resistance the aggressor finds, the more he enjoys his cruelty. Not always does he want to induce pain; he may enjoy producing an affect such as fear, rage, helplessness. Sometimes he enjoys overcoming the victim's resistance. Often the victim's begging and screaming is enjoyed, and eventually complete submission makes him feel elated and triumphant. Necrophiles enjoy the complete lack of resistance in the dead. Lust-murderers encounter the strongest resistance and enjoy overcoming it by killing the victim.

The misleading assumption was that active and passive cruelty—sadism and masochism—were thought to be two different instincts. But already Krafft-Ebing (7) considered them two different manifestations of the same drive. It is characteristic of the bipolarity of an instinct that both manifestations of it are present in the same person—hatred and love, fear and desire. Normally two such contrary manifestations are in balance with each-other. Sado-Masochism is a compromise solution of the otherwise insoluble problem of two contradicting drives. Masochism can be considered original sadism introverted by guilt.

The drive for cruelty is within the individual. It may be connected with power, but is not identical with it. Many persons in high rank had power but were free from any signs of cruelty. Tyrants have been described as serene and self-confident. They were full of aggressive activity, which could be considered normal, even desirable, as long as it was just aggression. Huge armies were organized, conspicuous buildings erected. Not always was this coupled with the desire to destroy.

Cruel people have sometimes come to exert brutality within the relatively narrow circle of family and friends. Those, who did not have great physical strength resorted to killing with poison—sometimes with the sole motive of experiencing power over life and death. In the history of the London Tower (8) we find numerous examples.

Hume, Hobbes, and Kant postulate that it is the contrast between one's own feeling of power and the feeling of the victim's helplessness, which is enjoyed. To observe the pain of others causes pleasure. One's own suffering appears to diminish upon the contemplation of other people's pain. Imagination helps people to suffer with the sufferer. One is glad not to be in his situation. That is supposed to be one of the reasons why people like to witness cruelty such as executions or flagellations. The San Francisco Examiner of April 9, 1968 carried an article headlined "Viet Crowd Sees Smiling Execution." Nguyen Van Thuc was the second man shot to death in a week. The crowd numbered 1000, mostly women and children. Some even hung through windows to get a clear view of the last moments of Thuc. Photographers climbed upon the coffin. Afterwards the crowd streamed out through the gates where vendors selling cold drinks and dried fish had many customers. After such excitation people experience a soft feeling of relaxation. We have the custom of eating and drinking after a burial. The family and friends assemble and behave as if they think—let's eat and drink and be glad that we are still alive. In former times a phallus was placed upon the grave to indicate that life dominates over death. That was the origin of gravestones.

Even though many people undoubtedly are gratified at seeing others suffer, it is hard to fully explain the satisfaction many individuals, who are not especially cruel, experience at the suffering of others. Many tender females enjoy going to the circus. Apparently the danger in which the artist there finds himself, is pleasantly in contrast with their own security. Achelis (10) in "Ecstasy in Religion and Art" states that unusual situations lift us up from our dreary everyday-life. However, this does not explain the phenomenon, since there are other cultural ethical activities that can lead to ecstasy, such as art, music and traveling. Furthermore, for people like Tiberius, cruelty was nothing unusual, it was part of his everyday-life. Only such individuals would select cruelty in order to achieve ecstasy, who already have an increased cruel inclination.

There are precipitating situations for cruelty, like war—when robbery, killing and seduction of helpless women and children is sanctified by the State. In such cases the State assumes responsibility; one's own conscience is lulled asleep; the State, greatest authority on earth, assumes the responsibility for good or evil and gives permission, just as parents would permit a child to kill insects which destroy the harvest; the child would then not question, but gladly obey.

Cruelty is a passion which can awaken suddenly even in ordinary, healthy normal individuals. It is innate and latent in every being. Apparently it is not just a lack of feeling or empathy, but pleasure in inflicting suffering. Philosophers could not completely explain this passion. It appeared to be irrational and could not be motivated by reason. Bain (13), Shaftesbury (11), and Charcot (12), stated that cruelty is inexplicable.

CRUELTY AND SENSUALITY: link with sex-drive, sodomy; influence upon foetus, example, case history—orgasm in slaughter house; cruelty in primitive cultures.

Krafft-Ebing (7), Moll, and Jaeger drew our attention to the close link between cruelty and sensuality: They emphasized that those rulers, who became famous for their cruelty, were also known to have a high grade of sensuality. During sexual excitement even normal people are inclined to commit cruel acts: Men squeeze and press the desired female, and kiss her until she almost suffocates. At the height of orgasm they may bite her without even being conscious of it.

Similar actions can also be observed in animals. It is known that certain kinds of spiders eat their partners during the sex act. The female spider takes the active part in copulation. The female Mantis religiosa tears up and eats the male. Some Crustacea are supposed to act likewise. The male canary often tears up the nest during the mating time, strewing the eggs around and eventually killing the female. The rooster pecks the hen on the back of the head. The tom-cat bites the cat on the neck. Some female fish beat their heads against the tail of the male. Tritons lay their heads against each other, the male hitting the female with his comb.

This seems to indicate that the sex instinct and cruelty are intimately linked. The passive partner often appears to enjoy such treatment; his excitement is heightened by it. Active and passive cruelty are part of courtship, and, like other courtship display, help to stimulate and synchronize the pair for copulation. (14)

The Romans' sensuality was excited by great spectacles during which slaves were torn apart by wild animals. Prolonging agony, accentuating the murderous effect of arms, and dragging out unforeseen episodes of deadly suspense developed into an art.

It can not be doubted that sexual gratification was caused by these games as nowadays by various sport-events. Cockfights and turtle-races appeal to the same instincts. During bullfights one can easily observe how excited the spectators become; men and women press against each other; their faces are flushed; wild ecstasy is expressed in their eyes; they scream with excitement. Malebranche cites the case of an idiot, inmate of an asylum, whose skeletal system had been deficient since birth. It was believed in the hospital that his mother—highly pregnant—had been impressed when witnessing the execution of a criminal, and that the foetus had been affected by this. Nowadays the diagnosis in this case would probably be osteogenesis imperfecta congenita. It is entirely conceivable that this severe phenotypic expression of an otherwise potentially merely latent genotype was brought about by the mother's experience. Modern medicine tends to consider such unproven statements as made by Malebranche merely "old wives' tales." However, similar occurrences have been reported by others. Lavater (16) describes the case of a mother, who after watching a criminal's hand cut off, gave birth to a baby born with one hand. The other hand was expelled with the placenta. Lavater observed that the mother's emotional state was more susceptible to the imagination during pregnancy. It is often observed during wartime that mothers sense danger approaching their son on the exact hour of his death. Experiments at Duke University have confirmed that people in close emotional contact can sense each other's perceptions at a distance. Researchers have found that the foetus is influenced not only by some physical diseases of the mother such as measles, but also by the mother's emotional state. The brother of the discoverer of the Salk vaccine using a special apparatus which produced sounds similar to heartbeats, found that even rhythm and sound exert an influence upon the foetus. Psychiatrists nowadays give great importance to the mother's state of mind during pregnancy, inquiring whether the child was wanted; and whether the mother was in a state of equanimity during pregnancy. Orientals have always ascribed to the prenatal chart an influence upon the character of the infant. It is possible that the mother's uncontrollable excitement causes circulatory changes and stimulates endocrine secretion such as adrenalin and that these changes influence the foetus.

Some women are reported to have experienced orgasm during bullfights. It is significant that elderly gentlemen and pretty ladies are offered bull's testicles—believed to be an aphrodisiacum—at the exit of the corrida in Madrid, Seviglia, Granada and Cordova. This shows that in those places it is well known that sexual feelings are aroused by viewing bullfights. In vain did the Popes try to abolish them. The most faithful sons and daughters of the catholic church remained obstinate and disobedient; the drive for cruelty was stronger than their religiosity.

In some countries it is customary to set animals at each other: Jumping of frogs, cockfights, and crabraces are still customary in various countries, including "modern America." Fish are incited to bite each other by instilling into the water a sharp liquid. Dogfights, dograces, horseraces, wrestling matches, and boxing matches—the latter not much different from Roman gladiator fights, all appeal to our instincts of cruelty.

Cruelty is so much a part of our everyday life that we are not even conscious of it: adults look surprised when children, accompanying them to foodstores, exclaim—"Oh, these poor little fishes!"

Domestic animals are often thoughtlessly exposed to cruelty: People have their cats spayed, their claws removed; dogs' tails clipped; ducks, geese and pigs fattened. At hunting parties the main goal is not always the provision of game for food, but the pleasure of chasing and wounding animals, which are not always caught but often left to perish. A horse may win the races but collapse. Birds are blinded in order that they may sing better. Millions of birds are killed to supply women's hats and garments with feathers. During the painful operation of removing horses' tails nerve fibres are injured and the animals groan and become frantic. Chickens and pigeons are often plucked alive. Fish-hooks and lobster-spears are pierced through living animals. Such methods of slaughter are not always expressions of cruelty but rather of indifference and lack of consideration.

19

Rousseau (17) describes how he gave a dinner-party at which all the food served was vegetarian. A lady insisted on having meat, whereupon he had a live chicken tied to her chair, asking her to kill it herself if she wanted meat; thereupon she gladly partook of the vegetarian dinner. Some vegetarians are thought to be masked sadists. They fight against their sadism; they can not see blood.

Cyril, a premedical student known for his cynicism and coarseness, was a vegetarian. He adhered to a special diet devised by Fletcher which emphasized extra slow and thorough chewing. On his first day at the dissecting table he collapsed because he could not see blood. He was unable to continue the anatomy-course and therefore gave up medicine. He changed to Law and later became a very aggressive district-attorney.

Perls (18) states that the use of the teeth is the foremost biological representation of aggression.

Teenagers, who grow up on farms, watching animals and not yet being informed about sex, sometimes indulge in intercourse with animals. Cases have been described of boys who introduced their penis into a chicken, enjoying the screeching of the hurt animal. Only seldom do such individuals lose control to the extent that they come to medical attention.

The nightwatchman making his rounds on the ship SS Marine noticed that the door of the freezer was open. On investigation he discovered the sailor Butch in close embrace with a frozen calf suspended from the ceiling. He was in such ecstasy that he was oblivious of the watchman's approach. He had just ejaculated against the calf's abdomen while gazing into its wide-open glazed eyes.

Investigation revealed that during his boyhood, when his grandmother came to visit, he had had to share his sister's bedroom. At first it came to some mutual sex-play, but then she got frightened and squealed. When he pressed his hand upon her mouth to stifle the noise she became rigid, staring at him, being completely in his power. At this very moment he had an orgasm. When grown-up he worked in a slaughterhouse, reliving the experience when seeing the blood and hearing the squeals of the animals being slaughtered. Being deprived of this habitual outlet while on the ship, he was under a compulsion to creep stealthily into the freezer at night when everybody was asleep. The frozen rigid calf with the glazed stare reminded him of his sister.

In our culture both partners usually agree upon the sex act. Among animals and primitive peoples force is often used; refined love does not yet enter into the unification. It is a remnant from the earlier stages of development of mankind that sex and cruelty are still linked. It need not necessarily lead to cruel acts; it may often merely be perceived in the facial expression, which often shows wild distortion during intercourse—pouting—grinding of teeth—grimacing. This goes back to former times when the male had to seize the female by force and although she at first resisted, she finally gave in. What formerly was essential to the sex play, is nowadays just used to heighten the pleasure. The female sometimes pretends to resist—in order to heighten the desire in the male. South Slavonian men begin the foreplay in intercourse by seizing the female by the ankles and throwing her backward; this procedure is enjoyed by her. A marriage custom in some Indian tribes specifies that a bride be treated so violently during her wedding-night that her jewelry is broken. Women in such cultures have a robust constitution and do not particularly suffer from this type of treatment. Many modern women would hardly survive if they were lifted up and stumped on the floor during labour after each pain as was customary amongst certain tribes. It should not go unnoticed that it was always the men who used such methods, and it can be assumed that they derived gratification from them. Such customs of primitive peoples were not always evidence of cruelty, but rather of uncivilized brutality. Furthermore the man considered his wife his possession. He represented the strong, stern, firm but protective father; she often remained in an infantile stage of development being completely dependent on him and willingly submitting to his every desire, especially since this was followed by his showing such tender love.

SADO—MASOCHISM IN THE ARTS: term coined after Marquis de Sade and Sacher-Masoch; representation in television, fairy tales, films, literature—Shakespeare, Rousseau, Victor Hugo, et. al.

The drive of cruelty, innate in every being, is so well covered up by civilization, that in our everyday life it is hardly noticeable. Still in the beginning of the twentieth century religious influence was so strong that sex was hushed over; nobody dared speak openly about sexology. That explains why the novels of the Marquis de Sade and Sacher-Masoch caused such a great sensation. They had the courage not only to write about sexual matters, but even to describe sexual aberrations. Henceforth the enjoyment of active cruelty, as described by the Marquis de Sade, was termed after his name—"Sadism" whereas the passive enjoyment of cruelty was called—"Masochism" after Sacher-Masoch.

The novels of de Sade (19) give detailed and lengthy descriptions of various forms of eroticism and in their time "Justine" and "Juliette" were considered a sensation. De Sade died in the beginning of the nineteenth century in a Paris prison. He was accused of various crimes, including sodomy and attempted murder. He is said to have suffered from schizophrenia during the last years of his life.

Sacher-Masoch believed that pain stimulates the sensitive nerves so excessively that eventually pleasurable sensations are experienced. He described how cruelty can split off the sex instinct and constitute gratification in itself; likewise can the desire to suffer become an independent means of gratification. However, he observed, that it is not completely indifferent to the individual on which part of the body pain is being inflicted; he found that parts in close proximity to the sex organs are preferred (buttocks, inside of thigh, anus, breast). Sacher-Masoch (20) externalized experiences and insights he had gained; he hoped to overcome his strong homosexual inclinations by getting married; despite his wife's objections he forced her repeatedly to have sexual relationships with his friends; this made him feel as if he were having intercourse by proxy with them. Such famous works as "Venus in Furs" grew out of their mutual experiences. Such details were described as for instance the excitement derived from seeing "Wanda" naked, a fur coat slung over her shoulders, emphasizing the contrast of the dark fur and Wanda's silky white skin. Sacher-Masoch's works were of higher literary and ethical quality than those of the Marquis de Sade. Nowadays their novels are mainly of psychological interest. The terms sadism and masochism have remained in use despite the fact that other authors like Rousseau and Dostojewski have shed more light upon the psychological mechanism of cruelty.

Rousseau (17) came to the same conclusions as Sacher-Masoch. He relates in "Émile" and "Confessions" how he was trained gradually by a governess to enjoy physical punishment until he finally provoked her to whip him. Wedekind (23) and Schnitzler (22) even presented the subject on stage. Krafft-Ebing (7) also believed aggression to be a normal component of love and to be but exaggerated in cruel acts. Havelock-Ellis (24) describes sex as "sinking into the great ocean of emotions." Eulenburg (25) believed man, trying in vain to fight his overpowering sex-drive, if frustrated, comes to have feelings of hatred for the female. It has puzzled many authors that cruelty and sex appear to be diametrically opposed—sex aims at maintaining life, whereas cruelty seems to destroy it.

Shakespeare (26) has represented cruelty and revenge in the "Merchant of Venice." Such works of art not only help us to understand people, who are different from ourselves, preventing us from feeling contempt and condemnation for them; but also help us to become aware of otherwise overpowering latent inclinations within ourselves. Goethe's (27) "Verses to Lili" depict Lili stroking her lover with her feet; her lover enjoys playfully subjecting himself to being treated like a dog. In Kleist's (28) "Penthesilea" a man is conquered and even killed by a woman. Grabbe and Heine present gruesome scenes in their works. The fear of sex drives a young man to murder in "The

Tell-Tale Heart" by Edgar Allan Poe (29). Hawthorne (30) symbolizes the danger of an attractive woman as a poisonous flower.

Artists have the gift of expressing what all people feel. Dostojewski (31) was predestined to further explore sado-masochism; he gained so much psychological insight that he laid the groundwork for psychoanalysis. He depicted life at the courts of the Russian rulers, especially of Katarina the Great, who was famous for her cruelty, and was called the "Semiramis of the North." He gained insight by critically analyzing his own life: His father died when he was a boy; having harboured deathwishes against his father he felt guilty and responsible for his death. He describes masochist tendencies in "Raskolnikow," explaining the connection between guilt and crime. In "A Little Hero" a lady takes delight in tormenting an 11 year old boy. In "Crime and Punishment" and the "Brothers Karamazow" Dostojewski masterfully describes how the mere will to kill—even though it may be unconscious—may lead to guilt feelings and self-accusations and finally prompt the conscience to seek punishment.

Boccaccio's (32) novels contain a wealth of sadism: In the "Decamerone" he recounts in detail how a husband beats his wife. D'Annunzio (33) in his novel "Il Piacere" portrays the hero as a great sadist. Zola (34) wanting to show nature as realistically as possible depicts a lady ruled by the desire to torture in his novel "Nana." In "L'Assommoir" and "La Bête Humaine" he recounts the deeds of a lustmurderer. Sudermann (35) created Salomé as a great woman-sadist; whereas Oscar Wilde (36) perceived her differently—having her kiss the cold lips of her dead John. In "Notre Dame de Paris" Victor Hugo (37) depicts murder and necrophilia, describing the crippled Quasimodo staying in close embrace upon the dead body of his beloved girl, with whom he had never had any physical contact during her lifetime. Flaubert (38) writes about sadism in his novel "Salambo." Maupassant (39) is known as a representative of erotic novels. He frequently chose subtle sadomasochistic topics. This is illustrated by one of his titles: "Fort comme la Mort." He was a drug addict and had a fear of open doors.

Myths and fairy-tales (49) are a remnant from olden times when mankind was still in its infancy. They contain many cannibalistic and necrophile scenes. They depict men falling in love with sick or sleeping girls. Self-mutilation such as gouging out of eyes, cutting off of toes, or castration is practiced (Little Red Riding Hood, Cinderella, Rumpelstilzchen, Hansel and Gretel). Myths and fairy-tales appeal to children: they see their own drives, not yet completely adapted to civilization, depicted in them. Witches, dwarfs, fairies, and cruel stepmothers can easily frighten a young child because it may not yet be able to distinguish between reality and phantasy. Small children often tell their mother in the morning how the spoons and plates in the kitchen talk to each other, or what the little bird in the garden just told them. Fairy-tales should rather not be told at bedtime, and we should explain to young children that they are not reality.

Some years ago it was reported that a farmer slaughtered a pig in the presence of his three year old son. The boy ran into the house, stabbed a knife into his newborn baby sister's neck—saying: "I want to see whether Mary squeaks like a little pig."

Nowadays film and television have taken over the introduction of children to cruelty. The movie "Last Summer" adapted from Evan Hunter's novel, shows how teenagers terrorize a pet bird and then a pet-friend. The adverse effect comic books and television may have on young children was already criticized years ago by Frederick Wertham (41) in his book "Dark Legend." He explained that children, being exposed to the description on television of death and murder for several hours daily, would of necessity become conditioned to cruelty. On one TV station he counted 334 killings presented during one week. Francis Rigney points out that youngsters nine and ten years old might imitate the actions of heroes they admired on television. The criminologist, Hans Mattick, was also repelled by the gruesome commercials on television. He was horrified by the movie "A Minute to Pray, A Second to Die." The film-producer Arthur Penn, is convinced that the success of his film "Bonnie and Clyde" was due to the brutality depicted therein.

The producer, Joseph E. Levine, shares this opinion, emphasizing that the success of a show depends upon the taste of the public.

A certain amount of censorship is justified where such media as television and comics are concerned, which are readily available at any time to children of all ages, without supervision. However, presentations on stage and screen help the average person to become aware of drives within himself which but vaguely felt were inexplicable to him. When sex was but poorly understood shows having it as their main topic were highly successful and drew much criticism. Now that the public is more enlightened concerning sex, interest in such shows has diminished. It is possible that if the drive for cruelty is no longer denied, but rather explained, presented, and fully understood we may be able to better deal with it. Once it is made fully conscious we shall no longer be overpowered by it.

It has been stated that nations—like individuals—have a conscience, an awareness, and a Self, delineating and distinguishing them from the rest of the world. The United States, a relatively young nation, has turned aggression outward. Only now are we becoming fully aware of our potential for violence; being fully conscious of the drive will help us to sublimate it.

EXPLANATION BY PSYCHOLOGISTS AND PSYCHOANAL-
YSTS: Freud, Groddeck, Menninger, etc.; oral and
anal stage of development—examples, case histories; fetishism; transvestitism—examples, case
histories; can we recognize sado-masochists by their
appearance? graphology.

The psychoanalyst, Groddeck, (42) stated "we are being
lived" by unknown and uncontrollable forces. Freud (43) believed, following his first investigations, that masochism originated from sadism which was turned upon the self. In "Economic
Problems of Masochism" he distinguishes three components—
erogen, feminine, and moral masochism. The desire to submit,
accentuated to the point of wanting to feel helpless and to
suffer, was considered the normal feminine attitude. In case of
predominantly masochist fixation this is accentuated into a desire
to feel pain. The moral component, if exaggerated, leads to
castration through guilt feelings, causing the sadist to turn
masochist. Only upon further investigation did Freud reach the
conclusion that man is constitutionally endowed with various
drives—amongst them a certain quantity of aggression. Aggressive drives are natural and necessary for the maintenance of
life. The social environment determines their form of expression. Eros and Thanatos are a polarity in nature and in the constitution of human beings. All psychic manifestations are bipolar; there is no love without hatred and consequently no
sadism without a certain quantity of masochism.

Psychoanalytic theories attempted to explain that a young
child is "polysexual." The sexual instinct, not as yet directed
towards a specific goal, derives gratification from all sorts of
stimuli. Stekel (44) warns parents not to thoughtlessly expose
children to exaggerated tenderness or to other overstimulation

27

such as tickling, slapping, scratching, biting, kissing, stinging, squeezing, poking,—since any kind of overstimulation can lead to a sadomasochist fixation. The desire to suffer—to feel pain— was termed by him "algolagnie." Fenichel (45) has described sadomasochism in culture and education, explaining that sadism derives from hatred which shows up normally in every child already in his first year of life whenever the baby is frustrated. When the display of hatred is not tolerated by the environment, the hatred may turn against the Self, manifesting itself as masochism; when it goes to extremes it may lead to self-torture.

A baby-girl, playfully hitting her mother's face, damaged her mother's eye. Not only was she severely punished, but she was also repeatedly criticized and derided by her parents and other members of the family. Consequently she developed the habit of pulling her hair to such an extent that she acquired numerous bald spots.

Moral masochism has been described by Menninger (46); he explains how guilt feelings may lead to self-punishment. It may not always result in physical suffering, but in humiliation and failure. The original desire to be beaten by a strict father may be transformed into the desire to be beaten by God or Destiny. It is an attempt of the ego to cope with a severe superego; a desire to endure in order to gain Father's or God's forgiveness. Freud and his disciples stressed the point that both active and passive trends regularly appear in one and the same person.

Psychologists emphasize how important the oral stage of development is for the formation of the individual's character. Spitz (47) first coined the term "anaclitic depression" referring to the reaction babies show when deprived of their mother's presence. As already demonstrated by Frederick the Great it may lead to death. Orality is the fundamental and most significant stage of development, the mother or substitute-mother being the most important person in the baby's life. If dependency needs have not been adequately gratified during this stage of development such children may feel helpless, inadequate, miserable, and angry. Even when grown-up they try to overcome any state of frustration by seeking to obtain oral gratification, often becoming alcoholics or drug addicts. Fromm-Reichmann (48) has aptly described this state of frustration as the "rage within." In such individuals dependency needs remain potentially strong throughout life just because they have never been gratified. Later in life they may identify with the handicapped and the "underdog." When their dependency needs are not satisfied in close interpersonal relationships, helpless rage may lead to suicide or homicide. Infants feel as if their own inadequacy is the cause of their frustration. These feelings of inadequacy and inferiority are carried over into adult life. They feel nobody loves them because they do not deserve it. All their relationships show great ambivalence.

Famina, a young girl in an Italian mental hospital, insisted on fasting because she was haunted by the idea that she had eaten her father. She had grown up without maternal care and attached herself so strongly to her father that she feared she had destroyed him by her oral-sadistic needs. She had believed the oral deprivation experienced during her infancy to be the consequence of her own hostility. Her mother had died in childbirth. Whenever she was disobedient her wet-nurse reprimanded her emphasizing that Famina was so evil that already when a baby she had killed her own mother. Fright and fear-dreams were characteristic reactions to her sadistic, cannibalistic phantasies,—the desire not only to identify with but to incorporate her only love-object—the father. Although she longed to be close to him, she felt relieved—while staying in the hospital —to be away from him. She reacted with hostility when he visited her, even refusing to go out on a short walk with him. She complained bitterly when he did not visit her for a few days, but showed her ambivalence when he eventually did visit her, "kissing" him so violently that she bit into his cheek, causing it to bleed profusely. Afterwards she had complete amnesia for this incident: such hostility would have been inadmissible to her—in her conscious state she would have disapproved of it. She had to erase it from her consciousness saying—"it was not me!" She withdrew completely into herself.

Many mothers, who have been seriously frustrated themselves

in early childhood, have sadomasochistic tendencies when grown-up and are overcome by infanticidal impulses towards their own children.

Barbie was the youngest of many siblings. Her mother died whilst giving birth to her. Older sisters cared for her—diapering and feeding her irregularly and infrequently. Her earliest memories were of feeling empty inside, and cold, wet and sore outside. She was a miserable, unhappy, whining child, at times screaming with rage. She remembered her childhood as a state of protracted isolation, during which she was continuously looking for somebody to take care of her. She developed mistrust of depending on others and endeavoured to depend only upon herself. At a young age she married a considerably older man, expecting from her husband what only a mother could give. She tried to trap him into a complete dependency bind, feeling murderous rage when she discovered him fondling their young baby daughter. She lost all ego control. Her jealousy led her to have infanticidal impulses. She was afraid to be alone with the baby for fear of hurting it. This resulted in guilt feelings and a fear of losing control. She was frustrated by her husband, who did not give her the "maternal" care she sought. Ego-alien murderous impulses were directed toward the husband and the baby. Once while attending to the baby she seized a kitchen-knife and was about to stab it into the screaming baby when she suddenly became rigid and immobile. She was afraid "to lose her mind"—to commit suicide out of guilt.

Analysts like Friedjung and Sterber explain that after the child has passed the oral stage of development it enters the anal stage of development and that for some reason—usually for some undue frustration—it may become fixated upon occurrences in the anal stage of development, when the desire to retain, to possess—not to part with an object—is very strong, and tactile sensations like grasping are very important. During this stage fetishism may develop. Fetishism and transvestitism are rather unexplored fields. By fetishism we understand the overvaluation of a certain object. The finer details of such object-choice have not yet been fully elucidated. Yet, such phenomena should not appear so very strange to us, since there are fluid transitions from what we all experience and consider normal—to what is regarded as abnormal.

Contemporary analysts like Menninger consider even nail-trimming and hair-cutting to originate in self-mutilation for cultural purposes. Hair had a special significance already in biblical times: Samson was supposed to lose his strength when his hair was cut off. Criminals' hair is still cut off. Tonsure is still practiced among monks. In Arabia and Syria hair was cut during puberty rites. Nero dedicated his first beard to Jupiter. Orestes offered hair at the tomb of his father. Hair was a symbol, standing for the whole body. Peruvian widows threw their cut off hair into their deceased husband's graves. We use expressions like "hairy ape." American Indians scalped their enemies, apparently deriving sadistic pleasure from it. Oriental customs prescribed different hair styles for single, married and widowed women. The gossipy atmosphere in barbershops and the torments women go through in beauty parlours still retain unconscious erotic value.

A young girl from a contemporary middle class family used to cut off a strand of her dance-partner's hair right in the middle of the dance-floor for the purpose of binding them closely and subjecting them to herself, asking them—"may I scalp you!" They did not understand what she meant but when she did cut off a strand of their hair they never objected for fear of attracting attention. She had a collection of hair samples.

Anthropologists explain the overvaluation of certain objects by the fact that the capacity for abstract thinking developed rather late. In primitive civilizations man was occupied with concrete things such as obtaining food and protection. He imbued a concrete object—something tangible—with certain qualities originally belonging to a person. Still nowadays this finds expression in various religious symbols such as amulets, rosaries or the Star of David. The symbol has a certain meaning for the person; sometimes even magic power is ascribed to it.

The director of an Italian university hospital, a well-known surgeon, wore a golden cross on a chain around his neck, next to his skin. He never took it off, not even when taking a bath. To him it was not just a piece of gold; it had a special symbolic meaning: His mother, who had died young, had put it around his neck when he was a boy, saying—this would protect him.

None of us is completely free of such beliefs and we should have no difficulty understanding them. All people cherish an object given them by a beloved person: Lovers exchange rings; when a soldier goes to war his girl may give him her handkerchief, saying: "This will protect you and you will come home to me safe and sound." He believes in the power of love residing in the kerchief. We all cling to certain objects which are dear to us. Maoris in New Zealand carry a Tiki in their money-purse, convinced that they will never be without money. The Tiki is supposed to represent an unborn baby, and just as a foetus still has unlimited possibilities of development, so would any person, who carries a Tiki. We can easily understand that only when such an object takes on so much significance that it depletes us of energy which could be invested more profitably, or when it takes on sexual significance, preventing a person from having normal sex activities, or when it causes the individual to get into difficulties with the law, can fetishism be considered abnormal. The person is often not fully conscious of the origin of his particular fetish; and usually only seeks psychological help when it causes him embarrassment.

At the beginning of therapy Tanner made an unusual request of his therapist: He wanted the therapist to go to a particular bar called "The Tool Box." On the wall there was a large oil-painting of a man in leather-boots. All the customers wore either leather-jackets or leather-boots. What bound them together was their worship for leather-articles. They could not give any explanation other than that it made them feel virile—masculine. Tanner explained that he became excited at the sight and smell of leather. He had felt embarrassed by it many times and wanted to work it out in psychotherapy. He did not know why it took on such undue significance but even his work was connected with leather: He imported suede jackets, saddles, and other leather articles. It had to be black leather. If it was merely plastic or imitation it had no effect on him.

It had to have the characteristic leather smell, and even the kind of shaving lotion he used was called "Russian Leather."

He had an embarrassing experience: At a party he squatted at the feet of a lady. He was wondering what had attracted him to this particular lady since she was neither young nor attractive. He was under a compulsion to stare at her shoes, which were made of black leather. He felt an increasing sexual excitement and to his great embarrassment urinated right there on the floor. Since there had been much merriment going on the incident was not taken seriously, everybody laughed and he was led out of the room by a friend.

Although he was not in the habit of kissing ladies' hands, he felt an irresistible urge to do so when they wore black leather gloves.

At a convention he and his colleagues gathered around the speaker after the lecture to ask questions. Approaching the desk he felt an irresistible urge to urinate into the lecturer's briefcase. Before he was even fully conscious of it he had already approached him closely, pushing aside his colleagues, who looked at him with bewilderment. Suddenly aware of his eccentric desire he was panicstricken and rushed out of the lecturehall. In his excitement, confusion and apprehension, he could not find the men's room. In desperation he entered the nearest telephone booth, where he urinated. Having attracted attention by his strange behaviour he was arrested. Being able to identify himself and explaining that he had weak eyesight and could not find the men's room, he had to pay but a small fine.

For several sessions of psychotherapy he did not bring any material that could have shed light on his strange urge, until one session when he suddenly leaped up to the interviewer's desk. Upon the desk there was a black leather briefcase in which the doctor kept documents. He began to stroke it, sniff at it, lick it, and before the doctor could ask anything, he had urinated upon the Persian rug. It was apparent that he was in a state of high sexual excitement, breathing heavily, and only when he had calmed down and was more relaxed he began to cry and was able to relate a long forgotten stage of toilet training: When his pants and diapers were being changed he was placed upon a cushion covered with black leather. He described his childhood as peaceful, kind of a paradise, and the gentle touch of his mother's tender hands when she powdered and rubbed his genitals with baby oil gave him pleasant sensations. But later his desire to be fondled was mixed with terror, when on one occasion he saw his mother's face, suddenly completely red, "her eyes popping out of her head," her heretofore soft and gentle voice was loud, shrill, stridulent, shouting words he did not understand. But the most terrifying thing was a huge safety pin which she was holding right in front of his eyes, and—the next thing she was going to do—he thought, she was to stick it right into his stomach. Actually he was not sure whether he just feared it or whether she did really sting him.

The fear and the pleasurable sensations and the smell of black leather had become welded into a complex, so that he tried to reconstruct a similarly combined situation. This explains why even his work was connected with leather and why he sought the company of other leather worshippers in the bar.

> Transvestitism is even a more controversial subject than fetishism. Transvestites, wanting to dress in a way that is customary for the opposite sex, are not always homosexuals. Fetishism and transvestitism sometimes blend into eachother. Transvestitism does not present such marked sadomasochistic features, and does not—like fetishism—develop during the anal stage, but usually through conditioning over many years:

A newly-married couple came to the mental hygiene clinic. The wife wanted to obtain a divorce, whereas the husband wanted to maintain the marriage. Both of them were working. One day upon coming home earlier than expected by her husband, the wife found him in a state of high ecstasy, in front of the mirror, clad in an eccentric evening gown, high heels, a wig, false eyelashes, and other make-up. Taken so much by surprise, it took him a little while to come back to reality. He admitted having a whole ward-robe of elegant female clothing and make-up kits in his workshop. The wife could not understand it. Arguments followed. He became impotent. During family therapy he was able to describe how this habit had developed gradually during his childhood: He was wondering about the transformation his mother underwent in the evenings: All day long she looked homely; she was a good housewife, working about house and kitchen in an old dress; but in the evening before the father came home, she underwent a real transformation: She dressed up, put on perfume and makeup, and put hairspray on her greying temples. Wasn't it a miracle that she was an ugly Cinderella during the day and became a beautiful princess in the evening? Wanting to see how that happened, he hid one night in the bedroom while she was dressing. He experienced a vague excitement when he saw her naked. He watched her sitting in front of the dressing-table, her beautiful face reflected in the mirror. He wondered whether he could change his appearance like that too? Later in the evening, when his parents had gone out and he was supposed to be asleep upstairs in his bedroom, he tiptoed downstairs, went into his mother's dressing room, put on her underwear and an evening-dress and all her makeup and walked up and down in front of the mirror, in her high-heeled shoes, imagining to be a woman. He found it very funny and exciting, and thereafter repeated this from time to time over the years. He was never found out. When he was older, he used to masturbate in front of the mirror on these occasions. His childhood was uneventful. His father was seldom home and did not impress him. He adored his mother and identified with her. He was delicate in stature and had a somewhat high-pitched voice. He married because that was expected of an average man, and he hoped he would not need the dressing-up game any longer. But although he was able to go through with intercourse on rare occasions, he did not derive much gratification from it, he never attained the same state of ecstasy. Over the years he had acquired expensive elegant evening-dresses. Somehow, he felt, it was degrading to have to conceal these activities and probably he subconsciously arranged to be found out by his wife.

His transvestitism did not originate through trauma or sudden frustration, but through faulty identification, since his father had no interest in the family, was seldom home, and did not care for the boy. His father was to him something distant and incomprehensible; since the mother made such an effort to please the father and subsequently was taken out by the father, he hoped to attract the father's interest by behaving like a woman. Therefore he developed graceful movements and spoke in a high-pitched voice which sounded like his mother's voice. Although he managed to get by unnoticed in everyday-life, he was not like other men, and we can consider this case as "moral masochism" because his activities were self-devaluing.

Some transvestites are hermaphrodites. Cases have been described in the literature of boys whose testicles had not descended into the scrotum at birth; the penis was mistaken for a clitoris; and the boy was brought up as a girl. Usually this is discovered at the age of puberty as was the case with a twelve year old girl in New Zealand:

She and her brother, who was a year older, had always been inseparable. The little girl was an excellent student and well-liked by her classmates. The parents were somewhat surprised when they were asked to see the teacher. They were informed that their daughter could not concentrate any more, could not keep up with the class;—had changed her behaviour:—she appeared introverted, generally disinterested and depressed. The brother also complained that she did not want to play with him anymore and had requested to wear his clothes. Once the mother's attention was aroused, she noticed that her daughter no longer cared for her appearance and had become negligent and untidy. Upon being questioned the girl could not give any reason for her changed behaviour, but began to cry and was inconsolable. The mother tried to console her. Upon entering the bathroom unexpectedly she could hardly believe her eyes when she noticed that the girl had grown a penis approximately two inches long. Subsequently the girl was examined by various doctors. Since she otherwise had all characteristics of a female, it was decided to remove it by operation. Thereupon the girl's behaviour returned to normal.

The question has often been raised whether it is possible to recognize sadomasochists by their appearance. Already long before the development of modern psychology, Lavater devised a system of classifying people according to their body-build and temperament. His principles were modified by Kretschmer (49) and later by Sheldon (50) in his "Constitutional Psychology." A person's temperament and susceptibility to certain types of diseases is related to his physical appearance. Corpulent people usually are easygoing and goodnatured; their movements are well-rounded, smooth and harmonious; their voices are soft. If cruelty is in their character-structure it generally appears as masochism, and if afflicted with nervous or mental disease, they usually tend towards being manic-depressive; whereas individuals of slight, thin body-build may be inclined to show sadist character traits, and if afflicted with mental disease they more frequently tend towards developing schizophrenia. Their movements are somewhat abrupt, sudden and jerky; their voices are more highpitched and stridulent. Shakespeare must have observed this and known it from experience because in "Julius Caesar" he expressed suspicion of "hollow-eyed" Cassius, having Caesar say: "Let me have men about me that are fat." It is not surprising that Marquis de Sade was of delicate appearance; his way of dressing was sophisticated and his handwriting looked feminine. However we can not completely rely on these theories since some of the worst tyrants have been corpulent.

Graphologists endeavour to detect active and passive cruelty in handwriting. According to Koester (51) ("Handwriting in Mental Disease") it is difficult to differentiate sadism from general aggression, whereas Wieser (52) in "Handwriting of Criminals" explains that several characteristics may be present in a person's handwriting which indicate excessive aggression, giving at least a disposition to crime: general disharmony of the writing, infantile level of forming letters, great disparity of pressure, rhythm, and direction, as well as emphasis of those parts of the letters which are below the line would all indicate that such an individual is easily swayed by any impulse and has no stability in his character, his willpower being easily broken. Graphology is gaining more importance as an adjuvant to character evaluation. In recent years Alfred Kanfer (54) in the

Strang Cancer Clinic in New York, has worked out a method of detecting early manifestations of cancer by examining handwriting by means of a special magnifying system. He also makes graphological evaluations for people contemplating marriage. If handwriting tests were given to school-children upon graduation, emotional instability could be detected at an age when the character is still plastic and proper psychological help given in time could prevent some character defects from being permanently established. Becker (53) supports this point of view, dealing with psychosis, neurosis, criminal inclinations, puberty, and the ability to concentrate in her book "Graphology of Children's Handwriting."

Most contemporary theories agree that active and passive cruelty are a fusion of two manifestations of the same instinct, and only when their relation becomes unstable can we speak of sadism and masochism. In cases where the normal sex drive is denied gratification, cruelty may increase and even stand in place of sex activity. It may restrict itself to phantasy, or seek gratification in reality. Whatever weakens our natural inhibitions, leads to increasing cruelty. A person, who is well able to control it in his every-day life, may become completely unable to cope with it when under the influence of drugs, alcohol, or jealousy.

An Eskimo couple appeared before a judge recently because the husband—in a fit of jealousy—had bitten off the tip of his wife's nose. When the judge asked whether she wanted a divorce, she protested vehemently, explaining how she loved him even more for being jealous and proving to her how much she meant to him, which increased her own value.

What is considered "normal" greatly depends upon the kind of civilization in which we live: the Indian ways of lovemaking taught in the Kamasutra (55) describe procedures such as growing a long nail with two sharp points in order to scratch the woman's breast, which is supposed to bring the woman into a state of ecstasy. This would hardly appeal to women in our cultural group.

Nowadays so many ways of gratification are forbidden that more and more energy has to be sublimated into higher goals and activities in the service of mankind. Freud has described how civilization leads to inhibition, repression, and eventually sublimation—in the service of humanity. Civilization has developed an individual conscience in man. Only relatively few individuals act out their antisocial drives and become criminals. Although mankind has fought for centuries against its primitive instincts in war we can see how thin the layer of civilization really is.

Since there are numerous subdivisions of mankind, men have identified with distinct and separate groups. Each has characteristic ways of life and religious customs, determined by historical development and geographical location. According to Joseph Bram (56) such groups are not definite but interchangeable. Defeat in war gives way to new boundaries. Sociogenetic evolution has split mankind into pseudospecies, tribes, nations, religions, and classes. The individual members identify with the group and hate all outsiders, saying the others are inhuman, different, in league with the "id" or the devil. A collective mass-conscience is formed. Authority usually succeeds in subduing individual conscience.

Marmor, Jung, Grinspan, and Schoeps (57) describe dehumanization of modern society and sadism in modern life. They agree that unresolved oedipal attachments to the father may lead the individual to subject himself uncritically to a group-leader—without questioning, in absolute obedience. In such cases State and Society become murderers. The leader, admired as formerly the father or teacher was, is imitated and becomes one's ego-ideal. The group-member wants to be accepted, loved, and to be especially close to the leader. One wants to be the favorite, as if to say—my father loves M E—my brothers are to be beaten. The group participants are to be aligned in a common front against the scape-goat group, often under-privileged minority groups. Sadists have often undergone persecution in childhood. They easily identify later with the scapegoat, but, attempting to defend themselves against their masochism, they may align themselves with the persecutor. The San Francisco Chronicle of July 16, 1968, speaking of the

Nigerian refugees, describes that thousands of men, women, and children arrived with broken limbs, eyes gouged out, hands hacked off, mouths split open. Pregnant women were cut open and their unborn children killed. Schools, churches, whole villages were burnt to the ground. Two hundred people kneeling in prayer on a Sunday morning were massacred. In Biafra there were four million refugees, three thousand of them dying every day. This demonstrates to what a disaster mass-cruelty can lead in our "enlightened times." To hate an individual is nowadays felt as disturbing because it contradicts the command to love one's neighbor as oneself. Therefore the individual hatred can easily be changed into social hatred. Once rationalized and sufficiently motivated by State or Government, there is no hindrance to social hatred any longer. One does not hate for egoistic motivations, but for one's nation or religion. It is no longer possible to easily engage in individual fights, as it was in former times, therefore another outlet has to be found to act out cruelty. Cruelty towards individuals may have diminished, but mass cruelty has even grown beyond all proportions. Now we can no longer conveniently blame God for whatever goes wrong in our life and if our world is destroyed it will be through our own actions. We can no longer deny the great destructive potential in human nature.

INFLUENCE OF RELIGION: oriental, western; martyrs; Fakirs; ascetics; suicide; circumcision; crucifixion; Penitence Order; self-castigation; Holy Rollers; Skoptsi; dancing manias; flagellation; Inquisition; gypsies; witches.

Investigating the various stages of development civilization underwent through the centuries, we can not overlook the strong influence religion has exerted upon the drive of cruelty. In ancient times men loved themselves in an animal-like, egoistic way, hating everything that opposed their wishes. Only gradually, as civilization set in, did men learn to love others. Love was gradually developed in men by fearing their Gods and sacrificing to them. People parted reluctantly with what they were to sacrifice. Only gradually did they learn to enjoy giving. Sacrifice was like a business: when people were afraid they sacrificed, but blamed their Gods when they were not assisted by them. Gradually man identified with others; first his own family; then his school-group, his social group, his country. He was ready to die for what he loved, but still only when compensated for it in "Heaven." Fasting and renunciation of sex were often demanded.

Most religious usages originated out of fear. Fear of God is still considered the most necessary quality in contemporary religious man. Primitive peoples feared their Gods even more. Everything was done to pacify the deity. Among all kinds of sacrifices even children were offered. People inflicted pain upon themselves, assuming that this was pleasing to the Gods. No wonder that we find gruesome forms of sadism and masochism in various religions. We must not forget that the cults were created by human beings and that their actions were influenced by their drives: a cruel priest—though he may have the best intentions—is easily led to carry over to the form of the cult his cruel drives.

41

It has been stated that human sacrifice developed as follows: Captives of war were usually offered to the Gods out of gratitude for victory. Also one was supposed to sacrifice that which one valued most, and that was one's children. Waitz (58) described in detail how the most beautiful virgin was sacrificed at intervals of three years in Bomy to JuhJuh: the priest bit off part of the falling virgin's head.—The sadist connotation is evident. In descriptions of contemporary lust-murders we often find that they bite into the flesh of their victim.

To understand human sacrifice better we must consider that proper family-life did not exist in the beginning of civilization. Consequently what we understand by "members of the family" did not exist in those days. The father made his children work for him. Wuttke (59) describes in "History of Paganism" that real family-life was seldom to be found. When parents did not like a child it was killed. Yet, still nowadays we sometimes hear angry parents shout at their children—if you don't obey, I'll kill you. It may not always have been such a terrific sacrifice for parents in ancient times to sacrifice their children to the Gods, especially in those countries where the soil was not fertile and great labour was required to procure food. It is a sad fact —which however can not be denied—that almost all peoples on earth sacrificed human beings, and especially children. Even in Greece those Gods to whom demonstration of respect and homage was shown later, were offered human sacrifice. We need only remember Chronos, who ate his children. Some examples in the Bible are well-known: Mesas, King of Moab, when attacked by the kings, Jehuda and Edom, sacrificed his eldest son. The Phoenicians sacrificed children. In the excavations of Megiddo numerous clay-jugs containing mummified babies bearing marks of sacrifice, were found. The best known example in the Bible is the sacrifice of Isaac by Abraham. We can consider it an act of atonement by Abraham for having let himself be influenced by his wife, Sarah, to drive his first-born son, Ishmael, together with Ishmael's mother, Hagar, into the desert. This episode can also be considered a protest against human sacrifice since an animal—a ram—is substituted for Isaac. The same tendency can be observed among other peoples, e.g. when

Agamemnon wanted to sacrifice his daughter, Iphigenia, the deity Artemis saved her, spiriting her away to the Taurians and substituting a stag. The Gods were considered almighty and cruel. Man had to submit to their requests, to their trials, to the superior power of life. The tale of Job shows sublimated sado-masochism.

The World Medical Association reported in 1968 a currently practiced Nigerian custom: "heartbreaking superstition surrounding the death of a mother at the time of childbirth: if the mother dies and the baby lives, the child is considered a 'killer-baby' and no woman will take it to suckle or raise. Usually these babies die of neglect within a few days."

It is not so rare nowadays, although less conspicuous, that parents rid themselves of their children although this may not be done in sacrifice: people often indulge in sex activities without taking precautions against conception and, being unable to care for their offspring, abandon them, place them for adoption, or even kill them.

Recently two children were found in an elegant San Francisco hotel, abandoned by their parents. When eventually the grandparents were found, they too refused to take care of them.

A married couple, having three children, was considering divorce, when the wife started—what the husband described as table-hopping. She felt that her eldest daughter, approaching puberty, was a competition to her, and would hinder her in her further plans. Therefore she made several attempts to drop her at a mental hospital: To that purpose she had the child examined by two psychiatrists in private practice, who both declared that the child was healthy, but that she—the mother, was in need of psychotherapy. Then she tried to declare the girl an epileptic, but did not succeed since she had never had any symptoms of epilepsy. The mother felt greatly relieved when the husband offered to take custody of the child. Manson, founder of a hippie-group addicted to murder, had been abandoned by his mother, a prostitute.

The roots of modern events can often be traced back to ancient customs. Harmony and dignity were completely abandoned during the festivals of Dionysus, which were celebrated in Sparta, Thebes and Delphi. The Menades destroyed whatever came in their way; small calves and deer were eaten raw. The unhappy singer, Orpheus, was killed and torn apart by Menades during the Bacchanales. Priests of the Phrygian goddess, Cybele, mutilated themselves in esctasy during the festivities.

In the fourteenth and fifteenth centuries the dancing manias, in which even children took part, became customary. Real dance-epidemics erupted in various places, especially during religious festivities. This was expressed in names like St. John's Dance, St. Vitus' Dance. It is said that people, who had a sedentary occupation, like shoemakers and tailors, were befallen by it. Nowadays we believe that—the more the life-instincts are frustrated, the more they tend to erupt with violence. The dancers lost control of themselves, got into a frenzy and often broke their heads, running into walls, or throwing themselves into the water. Those reports which emphasize that virgins and pregnant women participated, seem to confirm that frustrated instincts erupt with violence.

Growing civilization, as we have seen, repressed sex instincts more and more, and they found no outlet until they erupted with violence, and became uncontrollable. A considerable number of young girls became pregnant during those festivities. During a later epoch, when the polka became a fashionable dance, it was described that many people danced it so wildly that some succumbed to heart attacks. Some rather wild dances of our times can hardly conceal their origin from sex-drives which are sublimated in order to be socially acceptable activities.

Dancing-epidemics spread all over Europe during the seventeenth century. They were known by various names. In Italy it was called Tarantism and thought to be caused by the bite of the tarantula—spider. This kind of spider is still to be found in Italy, but people bitten by it nowadays, never get a dancing mania. It must have been a mass-suggestion. The participants reported that the dances led to lustful sensations, but many were found among the dancers, who had never been bitten by the spider. It became a real plague. Nowadays dancing—and marijuana-parties present the same characteristics. People, feel-

44

ing frustrated and unhappy, are looking for some kind of outlet and take recourse to drugs to achieve ecstasy.

In countries where nature gave people more than the bare necessities of life, where the soil was fertile and they had superfluous riches, a glut of the world, abnegation and renunciation are characteristic trends of philosophy and religion. Apparently, in order to be happy, man needs to strive and fight for attainment and happiness.

Indian religions recommend abnegation, renunciation of satisfaction, favouring negativism. Pain and gradual destruction of the body are depicted as the content of life on earth; and since no work is required to modify conditions in the outside world, modification of the spirit and inner life are held up as the goal of life. In these cults the lust for pain finds no inhibition. Although the Brahmin and Buddhist teachings are different, they completely agree that killing of the senses leads to complete ascesis. Exercises of penitence, such as rolling on the floor, have been taken over and modified in other countries, e.g. by the sect of the "Holy Rollers."

A man, belonging to this sect, had married a woman, who had an illegitimate blind child. He hoped to attain peace of mind by atonement for his sins. However, he did not succeed in repressing his drives, soon becoming unfaithful to his wife, taking refuge in alcohol and drugs. Hoping to atone for his misdemeanors by subjecting himself to self-inflicted suffering, he locked himself up in a room, whipping himself severely. When he did not succeed in killing his sex-drive, he came to hate his wife, and acted out his hatred upon his blind, helpless stepson, placing toys in his way, calling him "stumbling bum" and punishing him when he fell over them.

Practices considered desirable, admirable among some groups of peoples may be considered extravagant and may even be condemned by other groups. An elderly citizen, having been instructed in yogi exercises against high blood pressure, had been informed that by standing on his head a little while each day his blood vessels would be exercised and his heart would have less work. He practiced breathing exercises every morning in his garden, stood on his head, walked on his hands, and also said a morning-prayer. His neighbors, being perturbed by what they regarded as blasphemy, informed the police that there was a "crazy guy, dangerous to himself and to others." The man was thereupon brought to the State Hospital's observation ward in handcuffs.

Another exercise of penitence—to stand on one's toes for days—was modified by a catholic priest in California recently, ordering a homosexual, who came to confession, to kneel on dried peas during the whole night.

Religious Indians can be observed sitting under the rays of the glowing sun daily without interruption or exposing themselves naked to the cold rain. Such practices can be considered slow suicide. Ensuing illness is considered a step towards unification with Brahma. Such exercises, although no exception in India, can be regarded as outspoken masochism, often aimed at freeing oneself from feminine identification, e.g. in the case of Houdini, who attracted much attention even in the western world by his ability to extricate himself from all sorts of shackles. He confessed that he had been overattached to his mother and described the suffering and final gratification he experienced when struggling free from these shackles. Fakirs, asking to be buried alive, stated that it felt like being in the womb. They renounced any effort to maintain themselves, completely relying upon others to take care of them and supply them with food, as we do in childhood.

Sometimes this type of sadomasochism contains a strong element of exhibitionism as e.g. in the case of the bartender, Mike Meany, described in the San Francisco Examiner of April 22, 1968. He had himself buried and received air through a steel pipe, feeding on a chicken-diet, vegetables and Vitamin B_1. He had himself taken through the street while still in the coffin to the pub where he worked, shaking hands with people while girls danced. Whereas he had worked hard and lived in very modest circumstances, he now received an offer of twenty-four thousand dollars for acting in "disappearing acts" in a chain of hotels. The same article describes how Patricia Haverland even had a telephone inside her coffin and enjoyed answering the many calls that came in after the number was published in a local newspaper.

Great attention was attracted by Haridás, who submitted himself to medical examination. He was able to reduce all functions of life and stay without food for two weeks. However, he was placed in a cool environment, covered with earth, and from time to time revived by his disciples with applications of warmth. Braid (60) in "Observations on Trance by Human Hibernation" explains this as a kind of autohypnosis and subsequently induced reduction of body temperature. It can be regarded as a forerunner of hypothermia and cryotherapy of our times.

Ascetics have attracted much attention; their exercises show outspoken masochistic trends. Some ascetics deprived themselves of food; others lay upon a bed of nails. Of Buddha it is reported that he left his family, gave up his possessions, restricted intake of food, and pressed his tongue against his gum in order to symbolically maintain thought-processes. Repeatedly priests are admonished to voluntarily submit to pain and death. Historians report that some yogis stood motionless for years with their arms lifted up, and their fists closed, so that their nails grew through their hands. Still nowadays it is customary among certain African tribes to atone for misdeeds by holding an extremity in such an unnatural position for such length of time that contractures and deformities result. Among the Indians self-torment went beyond the limits of reason; birds nested in the yogi's hair and insects covered his body. Others cut their eyelids, staring into the glaring sun until they became blind. In such practices the masochistic desire for castration can hardly be overlooked. We must consider that they have to renounce gratification of sex at an age when the drive is most powerful. Some fakirs actually castrated themselves, hoping to kill their sex-drive. We can observe similar occurrences in prisons because no sexual gratification is available there. The sex-drive has been said to be stronger in tropical climates. From Kamasoutram—the Indian handbook of methods of love-making, we learn of practices appearing unusual and refined in comparison to our methods. In India, the land of contrasts, we find the deepest ascesis, and on the other hand the greatest lust. The heat of the sun, the poesy of the moonlight, filled with the smell of lotus-blossoms favoured the role of the poet, philosopher and impractical dreamer. Great passion is converted into ascesis through denial of gratification. The very drive, manifesting itself aggressively directed towards the partner, is masochistically directed against the self. Traveling reports describe Tapasvinas carrying heavy iron-chains on their naked bodies, others lifting up their arms, holding on to the branch of a tree until their arms, deprived of normal circulation, look similar to the branches of the tree. One fakir was observed going from Benares to Jagernatha repeatedly throwing himself down and getting up again. Such practices can also be observed in Mexican penitents at Guadalupe in modern times, worshippers sliding to the altar upon their knees, sunken in ecstasy, oblivious of pain, blood and dust. The Aissauas eat cactus-leaves covered with thorns, iron-nails, and glass-splinters; but they have trained themselves in such a way that no harm comes to them through such practices.

Defiance of authority is a characteristic many martyrs have in common. It may lead to death, or to punishment and suffering, or to self-destruction.

The erotic component of suicide has been stressed by Menninger in "Man Against Himself." People often arrange suicide in such a way as not to succeed. Repeated attempts are sometimes aimed at punishing a member of the family. Just as children are rewarded for sacrificing their egotistic wishes, the martyr finds reward in suffering for some ideal—be it religion, fame in science, conscience, country, or heroism in the "other world." In modern Buddhist demonstrations people ignite themselves as human torches in protest against war or governmental regulations. The recent deaths of nine persons in a single day as a result of family-suicide has focused new attention on Japan as the "land of Hara-Kiri." Tokyo recorded three thousand suicides in one year. Only a few disembowel themselves in the traditional way. Predominantly three types of suicide are recognized in Japan: *hara-kiri* is performed when dishonor has been brought upon oneself; *junshi* requires family members and servants to follow the head of the family—this occurs relatively seldom, innocent children are the victims in family pacts; *shinju,* the mutual suicide of unhappy lovers, is still common.

Nearly all the world's major philosophers, lawmakers and psychologists have wrestled with the moral, legal, and practical questions which arise when a person takes his own life. In ancient Greece the body of such a person was not cremated and his hand was hacked off. Pythagoras viewed humans as being the "chattels of God," having no right to leave this world without His permission. Plato, Aristotle, Virgil, Caesar, and Ovid considered it an act of cowardice. Socrates upheld the view that the will of the Gods could be made manifest and he acted accordingly, taking his own life. In Roman law it was not considered a crime. The early Christians, morbidly obsessed with death, committed suicide in large numbers for religious reasons. St. Augustine argued that suicide was a violation of the commandment "Thou shalt not kill." In the late thirteenth century the church denied a suicide burial in holy ground. With the Reformation impetus was given to freedom of thought. Schopenhauer and Nietzsche were in favour of freedom to dispose of one's own body. Lombroso and Spencer postulated that the individual was sovereign over his own body and mind. By the middle of the nineteenth century most European nations had abolished penalties for suicide. In spite of this generally-accepted opinion that suicide is not considered a crime, there are still today on the statute books of various States and Nations laws regarding suicide a crime, and assisting a suicide aiding and abetting a crime.

Freud explained that hatred directed against an external object may turn back upon the Self. If aggression is directed against another person, the result may be homicide; if turned inward, the result may be self-destruction. An individual, thrown into a panic, when his ego-structure succumbs to undue stress, may take his own life in an abrupt manner, giving the appearance of its having been an accident. In contrast to such sudden imbalance we see slow protracted forms, wherein depression increases steadily when repressed, subconscious material—becoming conscious—is unacceptable. The individual then shows self-derogative tendencies, self-accusations, doubts, and self-contempt. Unable to establish relationships with his fellow human beings in such a defensive state of mind, he may be driven into stupor, despondency, or hunger-strike.

Reik (61), following in the footsteps of Freud, pointed out that social masochism originates from sadism, which in turn, under pressure of fear and punishment, turns against the Self, e.g. During World War II bomb-attacks in England were met with admirable stoicism, whereas in Berlin whole families committed suicide during bombing attacks; in a panic parents killed their children and then themselves. It has been assumed that the laws against suicide were unconsciously rooted in the wish to protect the community against mental contagion, since it had been observed that suicide could start a chain reaction. The present trend in law in most countries is that neither suicide nor attempted suicide be considered a legal offense, but that it may be advisable to detain a suicidal person in order to provide medical treatment.

Factors similar to those held responsible for suicide may lead to sacrificing but a part of the body. A most peculiar expression of sadomasochism, originating in primitive tribes and reawakened in our own time, is circumcision. In olden times it was justified by stating that orientals have a longer foreskin, which permits the accumulation of smegma, especially in a hot climate. However, uncircumcised Persians, Indians, and Africans retain their health even in hot climates. In ancient times cleanliness was not too highly regarded. Circumcision may be equated with sacrifice of blood, made to the Gods, as Abraham stated in biblical times; that particular part of the body, which was highly valued and considered a symbol of fertility, was partly sacrificed. Some peoples practiced circumcision not on newborn babies but on young boys at puberty. Castration and circumcision were integral part of the Phrygian ceremonials. Self-mutilation was also practiced by Syrians. The cults of Cybele and Attis, Zeus and Hekate, Adonis and Osiris are often cited as famous mythological examples. In the Orient eunuchs were entrusted with the harem. The priests of Baal mutilated themselves. Youths were sacrificed at the altar of Artemis. In Tonga it was common practice to cut off a portion of one's finger in order to attain recovery of one's dear relatives. In China, Bengal and among the Peruvian Indians blood sacrifice was believed to save the life of sick people. The Ekhili in Africa practice circumcision before marriage: the foreskin is pulled out in the presence of the boy's parents and his bride. Gobineau describes how tetanus often set in after such procedures and the victim died within a few days. Cruelty of priests in ancient times aimed at restricting the sexual instinct.

Christian religion has often played an important role in inflicting cruelty. In "Sermon on the Mount" it is advised—if you have sinned with your eyes, pluck them out. This goes back to olden times: Oedipus, who blinded himself, had seen what he should not have seen, known what he should not have known.

Forgetting and repressing is still an attempt at self-cure: Schizophrenics often cathect like this *one* specific part of the body, tearing out their eyes or hacking off their hand, foot or ear; a well-known example is the case of van Gogh.

From the times of persecution of the early Christians we need only remember the martyrdom of holy Agatha, which took place in 251 under the supervision of the emperor, Decius. Agatha, born in a noble Sicilian family, was of rare beauty, which incited the desire of Quintianus, governor of Sicily. When she did not comply with his wishes, he made her live in a house of ill fame; when he still did not succeed in seducing her, he had her martyred so cruelly that she died. Sebastiano del Piombo has depicted the scene in a famous painting: Glowing tongs were held to her nipples. The facial expression of Quintianus clearly depicts his delight in her torture. Looking at him, she spoke the historic words: "You who have been fed at a mother's breast,—don't you blush at inflicting such shame upon me!"

Human nature does not seem to have changed much during centuries; cruelty is still deeply ingrained in us, only the form in which it manifests itself has changed. Leading religions even created a formal codex of cruelty: We need only think of such occurrences as "malleus maleficarum." Love is supposed to be the guiding principle in Christian religions; they are not supposed to consist in passive contemplation like the teachings of Brahma, but in a life of action motivated by love. Suffering was recommended: only when a priest wanted to dedicate his whole life to his vocation, did he decide to renounce upon marriage. However, the adherents did not live up to such high standards, soon they had to be modified. Christ connected with his self-sacrifice a high moral goal: he wanted to improve the lot of mankind.

The malleus maleficarum shows that still in the fifteenth century people believed in witchcraft. Physicians, whose ointments or good interpersonal relationships cured patients, were immediately regarded as magicians; and astrologists or dream-interpreters, whose explanations were correct, were thought to be in conspiracy with evil spirits. Religion, family life, right and justice, ethics and morals were no longer adhered to. Beliefs in witchcraft, sorcerers and pacts with the devil had extinguished religion and ethical values.

In those times even the Pope fell victim to superstition. Innocent VIII released the famous "Golden Bull" (public document) "summis desiderantes," which declared that there were a number of individuals—male and female—who had physical intercourse with devils of male and female sex, and with such assistance were able to do all kinds of mischief. This document entitled three priests to eradicate the evil and it released a chain of tortures and murders following the slightest insinuation. Not contented with such results, they created a system or codex of witch prosecution, which described in detail the unification with devils on Sabbath. Special torture-chambers were installed by fanatics. When we read about people's agonies we are inclined to believe that such things could only happen in the "dark middle ages." Yet they were repeated in concentration camps in our "modern times," and no one, not even the Pope —"representative of God here on earth"—objected. This book, "Malleus Maleficarum," is now called by religious leaders the book of hell. It shows us again that human nature is composed of "heaven and hell," of good and evil; every instinct has two opposite components, and Christian religious leaders were not always guided by Christian ethical principles. Pope Stephen VI, famous for cruelty, ordered his predecessor, Formosus, to be exhumed after he had already been interred in his grave for nine months, had him clad in the Pope's attire, and instigated a court action against him. Following this the corpse was mutilated, dragged through the streets, and thrown into the Tiber. The populace was extremely enraged, Stephen was found strangled. John XI (931-935), illegitimate child of Countess Marozia, was followed by Ottavian, who was but seventeen years old (955-964). His way of life was so immoral that he felt compelled to choose a new name—"John XII." This led to all later popes assuming a new name when taking office. (Seppelt—Katholische Papstgeschichte) Since they set such a poor example it is astonishing that people had the strength not to imitate them. That century was called the "dark one." In the ensuing century the Popes strove for worldly power, the best known example being Pope Gregory VII, who made Emperor Henry IV stand in the snow three days (1077). Innocent III (1198-1216) set himself up as judge above emperor and nations. In the fourteenth century a French and an Italian pope were in power at the same time, fighting each other. Other religions were considered to be against the "group" and minorities persecuted, as still today. In 1184 the bishops were ordered to enquire about such "minorities," and to burn them; "inquisition" was the result. Suspect individuals were ordered to wear two yellow crosses on their clothing. We have not come far in the twentieth century,—when German Jews had to wear a yellow star. In 1252 Pope Innocent IV introduced torture, renewed in our enlightened twentieth century in Germany and Russia, not only used against Jews but also against gypsies, politically undesirable persons, and all those, who did not subject themselves to the generally accepted beliefs.

When Pope Innocent VIII (1484)—released the bull directed against witches, many an outstanding person was suppressed and even ignited, e.g. Jeanne d'Arc, later pronounced 'holy' by the Church. Such persecution still persisted in the seventeenth century. But still nowadays about seventy court-actions per year are conducted against witches, mainly in Great Britain. Prejudice is just a desire to believe, mixed with fear that the belief might be shaken. Fear of the Devil is fear of sin, fear of one's own evil drives; it is easy to understand why belief in evil and witches still persists. It was supposed to be the devil, who visited and terrified nuns at midnight; in this context Boccaccio recommends: "punish the devil by sending him to hell," but he calls 'hell' the vagina.

Humanists and atheists have by no means separated themselves completely from religion: they are morbidly interested in overcompensation of their religiosity by constantly discussing religious matters.

Marquis de Sade often indulges in describing the cruelty of priests, stating that under their masks of culture they conceal primitive hatred; he considers them infantile and social cripples; "Hell," he says, "is a projection of our inside feelings into the outside world." We may add—of our subconscious sadism. He has shown how religion can express itself negatively as blasphemy. Those, who identify with Jesus usually do not suffer for a moral goal as he did, but masochistically enjoy suffering per se, which is often over-compensation for originally being a sadist. A strong affect, such as ecstasy, can convert pain into anesthesia, (as in the case of Millie, [case history pp. 1-7]) since an excessive stimulus does not stimulate any further but leads to paralysis or shock. In ancient times operations were performed without anesthesia, and torture has been depicted in which the victim looked on with curiosity, no longer experiencing pain. The greatest masochist, however, can not endure even slight pain when it is outside the range of his affect e.g. at the dentist.

Jesus asked for the renunciation of evil, but not, as his followers did, for relinquishing Eros altogether. He loved his disciples, even his enemies. But when his followers expected renunciation of Eros, this created such displeasure that it gave rise to hatred. Love was split into spiritual and physical; and the latter was considered sin. Man was to renounce and to suffer; if all people were on the cross they could feel for each other; and that was an important stage in the development of western civilization. Primitive man was thoughtless, but not sadistic. To be a sadist, he must enjoy others' pain and his power over

54

them. Our reaction to others' pain is either indifference, compassion, empathy, mischievous joy, or lust. Empathy is supposed to lead us to feel others' pain as if it were our own. The scapegoat in ancient times served to divert hatred from oneself on to an innocent object. We have seen that adherents to the Christian religion did not live up to the main principles of their religion—to love their fellow-human beings. Indian ascetics can be considered egocentric because they do not bother about their fellow-human beings, being interested but in themselves. Christian ascetics would not mind their fellow-men being burnt in hell as long as they themselves live in eternity. The spirit of all-engulfing love did certainly not fill the hearts of ascetics and priests, neither in the 'dark middle ages' nor in our times.

Priests were to renounce fulfillment of the sexual drive and to sublimate it; to convert such energy into religous activities directed towards the benefit of all mankind. Not all of them were able to achieve this and in order to punish themselves they began to torture themselves. The ascetic, Evagrius, has become known by jumping into an ice-cold well and staying in it all night, when he was unable to otherwise overcome his sex-drive. His teacher, Makarius, fought sexual desire by staying naked in a swamp, where he was bitten by insects all over; upon return his whole body was so swollen that he was recognized only by his voice. Nitrius' name has gone into history because he fought his sex-drive by burning various parts of his body, so that he was covered all over by scars. Anachoretes preferred death as a means to overcome the sex-drive; they castrated themselves; one of them even rose to the rank of bishop.

Chains, rings, and iron-shirts were used even by women to combat sex. They cut off their breasts and mutilated their faces in order to avoid being seduced. An Alexandrian nun cut out both her eyes to repel a suitor, who had told her that she had the most beautiful eyes and by means of them had seduced him. Holy Ebba, abbess of the Convent of Coldingham in Scotland, followed by her nuns, cut off her nose and upper lip to protect herself against being used sexually by Norman seapirates, who had intruded into the convent. The monk, Giuglielmus Firmatus is said to have placed his arms into fire to prevent himself from seducing a female who attracted him. Robert Coelestinus was consumed by the desire to be united with Jesus and to die for him. He satisfied his longing by carrying into his convent-cell a treebranch shaped like a cross and hanging himself on it every day for a little while. Since in the hanging position the bloodflow into the lower parts of the body is increased, the hanging position leads to erection.

Until recent times some sects have practiced crucifixion not only as a means of attaining states of ecstasy, but even leading to death. Even women indulged in it. In 1823 Margaret of Wildenbruch, Switzerland crucified her sister in order to conquer Satan and subsequently she herself was crucified by her family. Some religious sects, presenting passion plays, show their adherents the scene of crucifixion in a realistic manner. Traveling-reports describe such scenes observed in Mexico:

A man, walking slowly, was beaten with a whip made of grass; it served to keep open wounds which previously had been cut into his back. The whip was periodically immersed into a liquid carried by a third man, in order to prevent the blood from coagulating. All three men were known as villains in the community, but by subjecting themselves to such treatment, they were absolved from all their misdeeds committed during the past year. According to reports by C. Steffens (63) New York, medical colleagues from Santa Fé confirmed that such performances still take place nowadays. They were performed especially by the Los Hernanos Penitence Order, which had been founded in Spain during the Middle Ages, and spread over other countries. Later remnants of it gathered in Mexico. The purpose of the order was to attain forgiveness of sins through mortifying one's flesh. Phelps in Las Lunas describes the following: A primitive hut is built near Morada. Inside the hut there are wooden crosses, each weighing about two hundred pounds. Members of the order, gathering near the hut, sing religious tunes while whipping themselves. Others carry the heavy crosses. They call themselves "Brothers of Light." Good Friday is chosen for these procedures. After the whipping the brothers of light are tied to crosses and branches of wild roses tied around their heads, thorns penetrating into the skin of the forehead.

The mayor watches the ceremony, which lasts about thirty minutes, then the victim is freed.

One of the best known examples of passive cruelty, where highly valued parts of the body are sacrificed are the rituals of the Skoptsi (64), a sect widespread in Russia. The basic principle of their religion is to serve God by sacrifice. Despite Government persecution their numbers have increased steadily. Although by their practices they hope to kill their sex-drive, they succeed as little as the fakirs do. They only modify it, and coupled with cruelty, it remains as strong and predominant as ever, only changing its form and mode of expression. Agents for this sect are to be found in every large city in Russia; they voluntarily expose themselves to the danger of being discovered, risking their lives. Everything, including persecution, force and bribe is tried to find willing victims. Apart from religous fanaticism they are driven by bloodthirst, so that each religious gathering culminates in the most gruesome horrors. They love to see blood, and a ceremony without blood-sacrifice has no attraction for them. Their ceremonies culminate in a wild dance of the whole community, continuing until they are completely exhausted. Beyond doubt the sex-drive has thus been converted into other ways of expression. During some special festivities passive cruelty changes into active cruelty as described by Haxthausen (62): The left breast of a fifteen year old virgin is completely removed, placed upon a dish, and eaten by the participants. A newly accepted male member of the Community may suffer the fate of castration, as described by Melnikoff.

The Russian government,—even before Communism, considered them a sect of lust-murderers, and postulated that a country in which such a sect might come to power and influence, would be doomed to destruction. The sect glorifies cruelty and bestiality. Stern describes how participants appear at their gatherings clad in white shirts. The ceremonies start at ten O'Clock in the evening, lasting through the night. There are no written liturgies or contracts. All members are obligated to keep complete secrecy. Tunes are transmitted by tradition, and often created on the inspiration of the moment. Haxthausen, who participated in one of their gatherings, renders a song as follows: "Hold together, navigators! Don't let the ship sink! The holy ghost is with us. His mother, Akulina Ivanowa, is with us. Christ will come. He will apear ringing the great bell Uspenskij. All real believers will be called together. Put up masts which will not fall; set the sails which do not tear; and build the steering-wheel that will guide infallibly." The song is begun by men beating the rhythm by slapping their hands upon their thighs. Then the women sing alone. The ensuing dance is called Radenije—ardency—work in God. There are four kinds of Radenije: the little ship, the little wall, the little cross, and man for man. "The little ship" is built by jumping around in a circle, pressing against each other's shoulders; "the cross" is made by dancing and hopping in rows forming a cross; dancing "man for man" is similar to the dances performed by dervishes standing in the same spot turning around themselves. Eventually all attain a state of ecstasy, indulging in holy kisses as commanded by Selivanov, the founder. If such customs appear strange to us, we need only remember that "holy kisses" are used still nowadays in the ceremonies of the B'hai sect. They serve to bind people of various races and classes closer together. The Skoptsis find satisfaction derived from such relatively harmless pleasure insufficient; wherefore eventually sadomasochistic orgies lead to the mutilation of young men and women.

Gradual steps of purity are attained by persons on whom mutilation has been performed. Court actions have brought out that the operation called "small seal" consists in the removal of the testicles; the "great seal" in additional removal of the penis. The operations are performed by specialists in such a skillful masterly manner that catastrophes seldom happen. Among five thousand four hundred and forty four Skoptsi, eight hundred and sixty three castrated *themselves*. According to the reports they gave at court sessions, the operation was usually performed in several sessions. A narrow catheter was introduced immediately to prevent adhesions and facilitate urination. Although women are under no obligation to have themselves mutilated, there is hardly an unmutilated Skoptsi-woman. For them too there is the great and the small seal: To attain

58

the first grade of purity, her nipples are removed; the second grade often is attained by removing one or both breasts and often the vulva is disfigured. However, this does not prevent pregnancy and even prostitution is common among them. Not only simple people belong to this religious order, but people from all walks of life. It is remarkable that some of the Skoptsi have attained a very old age: there are some of them who have attained the age of one hundred and ten years. Statistics have shown that the number of Skoptsi is steadily increasing. In the middle of the nineteenth century there were but two hundred known in Russia. By the beginning of the twentieth century there were about three thousand, although this refers only to those who came to the attention of the government. Haxthausen stated that if all the members were known one could arrive at at least twenty thousand. Most of them are said to be found in Petersburg, Kostroma, Rjaesan, Kaluga, Lursk, and Moscow. Some have been reported at Ssamara, Ssaratow, Bessarabia, Tambow, and Tula. Many of those who came before the court were banned to Siberia; others fled to Galicia and Rumania, where their main communities in Bukarest, Galatz and Jassy number at least twenty thousand. This shows that persecution did not lead to their extinction but rather that they may attain their goal—they state that when they have a numerous membership, the millennium will start.

The rituals of the Skoptsi give us insight into the duality of drives. Every person, producing both male and female hormones in his body, has both components in his personality. Skoptsi-men fight within themselves the female component of their character, projecting it outside; they feel sadistic towards women, but masochistic towards themselves. Their rituals are symbolic acts. Homosexual tendencies are repressed. Their rituals can be considered phylogenetic regression—sadism is combined with cannibalism. Blood, sperma, urine, liver, heart, and penis had been thought by cannibals to be the seat of the soul. They were believed to have magic power. Various religious usages were adapted to the requirements of the community. Skoptsi rituals show that they dictated punishment for impulses such as lust for murder. When hate- and love-elements are not well fused but in an unstable relation, ambivalence is an outspoken character-trait of such people.

We see again that the combination of religion and cruelty has its root in infantilism. When belonging to a group, the individual regresses in civilization. Fascinated by the leader, they rationalize that the cruelty they indulge in is in the service of a higher idea. As in all groups, individual responsibility is diminished since the leader has assumed it. Feelings of power are strengthened and identification with so many others help the individual to overcome feelings of inferiority; he becomes an automaton, blindly following the leader and primitive reactions can easily find their expression.

Various Skoptsi sects indulge in different religious customs. The Perewertyschy practice castration in children, combining it with twisting the spermatic cord. Another subgroup—the Prokolyschy, perforate the spermatic cord with a needle. In Belew a new subgroup was formed fairly recently; they call themselves Tombowists after their leader, Tombow. However, not being so conservative, most of them practice castration only after having procreated children with their wives. The Skoptsi are known for their wealth, and they gladly dedicate large sums to winning new members. Their organization is powerful and so much feared, that only very few deserters and traitors have been known. Whoever left them, sooner or later fell victim to their actions of revenge, regardless of his whereabouts. Even those, who took part in their gatherings out of curiosity could not be certain of leaving without some operation being performed on them. Some participants were tied to a cross against their will. Four hundred seventy castrations were known to have been performed in a single year in Russia. The Skoptsi, who succeeds in gaining twelve new members for the order, is elevated to the rank of apostle.

In order to deceive governmental authorities marriages are sometimes still concluded in old age with much younger women, who are permitted to have intercourse with younger men; but children born by such women belong to the order right from birth. A great number of recruiting officers is regularly employed and paid to enlist new members, and to buy small children for the holy castration. Those female Skoptsi, whose sexual parts have been mutilated, are considered to be like the holy virgin. When they give birth to a male child, the baby is considered the son of God and has to die for the sins of mankind. He is killed on the eighth day by piercing his heart. The blood is consumed and the body dried and baked into small breads, which are consumed on Easter Sunday, symbolizing the blood and body of Christ. Not only the Skoptsi and Chlysty kill newborn infants but also other sects such as the Gnostics, Barbeliotae, Borboriani, Stratiotici, Zachaei, and Messalini.

In other subgroups virgins but fifteen or sixteen years old are declared holy and used for sexual intercourse by various males of the sect. In case the girl is impregnated and gives birth to a male child, it is sacrificed as described. Four cases of this kind came before a Court in Odessa. The sects consider it a good deed to kill babies and thus spare them life on this earth, reigned by Satan. The Feodosians send their children to orphanages because they consider them witnesses of sin. One of their songs goes—"No happiness can be found in this world; death alone can save us; God left the world; let us return to him." Life on earth is thought a punishment and the birth of a child means misfortune. Suicides are held in high esteem.

Suicide is also an expression of the illusion of being omnipotent—master over life and death; however, it is not considered real death, but rather approach to real life, eternal life, life after death or a step towards reincarnation. Apparently there was the need for atonement not just in a few individuals but in the community. They believed that Adam and Eve sinned by entering into a sexual relationship. Whole communities were converted, even seventeen hundred at once.

The idea of renunciation of sex is present in all religions and has existed for centuries. Furthermore, all religions have used symbols to represent great entities. As we have seen, circumcision is a symbol of more radical mutilation; circumcision and castration were equated. Circumcision of women was

61

widespread among primitive peoples, (clitoris, labia majora or minora, or even all of these were sacrificed.) Puberty rites among aboriginal peoples consisted also in circumcision or acts such as knocking out teeth; among some tribes the boys were beaten by the men. These rites symbolize rebirth, so that after the ceremony they will have separated themselves from childhood and hardly remember it, the purpose being to detach them from childhood and their mothers and make them into men.

Skoptsi enjoy the fear of the victims and the power over them. The actual act of flagellation they practise need not last long nor be strong; intense imagination heightens the ecstasy.

The desire to venerate and to adhere leads to an attitude of humility in various Skoptsi sects, even though the venerated person may not always deserve such adoration. The leader enjoys being recognized and approved of by the group; it makes him feel important and special and he often displays exhibitionist tendencies.

Hopelessly sick people were welcome members; they were baptized and then left to die. In Charjkow a sect was discovered whose male members participated in tickling female members. The government tried to restrict the activities and increase in membership by imposing double taxes; but this led to innocent people being accused by their personal enemies of belonging to such sects. One of the leaders of the Filipones preached: the end of the world is near, Antichrist is reigning, do not obey the worldly government anymore, our persecutors are led by Satan, we are the servants of God. Another leader, Montanu, maintained that he was the Holy Ghost; he ended by suicide. Many imitated him; whole families set fire to their houses, burning themselves. A whole epidemic of fire-setting erupted. Two hundred forty alone burned themselves in Kargopol, six hundred in Nischny-Nowgorod. Domitian and Schaposchnikow made a name for themselves by following the Filipones' example. Other sects denied themselves food and perished from exhaustion. Some adherents distributed all their possessions and became nomads.

A red cloth is a means of recognition for the Skoptsi. Those subgroups which became nomads, used a red cloth in a procedure called "The Red Death."—If one of the nomads suffered from an incurable disease, he became a burden to his fellow-men because he was unable to walk with them and constantly change domicile. He was put to death by a fellow-member, by pressing upon his face a cushion wrapped in a red cloth and sitting upon it until the patient is suffocated. In the ranks of these nomads many deserters and ex-prisoners can be found. Under Nikolai I military service lasted twenty-five years. No wonder that the numbers of deserters grew steadily. They were glad to find refuge in the sects, the most famous one led by Nikonow. Considerable numbers of deserters fled from the revolution under Nikolai II to sects which had gathered near Jaroslav and Perm. They postulated that breaking the law meant harming and weakening the Antichrist.

Mutilation of breasts, as described, was not confined to Russia, but was practiced by Indians in North America still in the nineteenth century.

We can not consider mutilation of organs as something alien to our civilization if we remember that the catholic church practiced it until recently: In the chapel of the Pope there were a number of castrated boys, who were operated upon before the age of puberty in order to maintain soprano voices. Some Popes, e.g. Leo VIII, disapproved of it; but conductors of choirs, especially in the Sistine Chapel, were so delighted with the boys' voices that they did not want to dispense with the custom. Napoleon forbade it, calling it barbaric; but later popes introduced it again. The Jesuit Pater Tamburini states: "Castration for the purpose of praising God by these beautiful voices is fully justified. Such examples demonstrate again how religion led to many aberrations, which were not conducive to promoting civilization."

Some convent cells contain a veritable collection of torture instruments. The case of a nun becoming pregnant in the convent of Wettun attained some publicity. She was imprisoned and fed on bread and water. The priest, who had impregnated her, was castrated. In the fifteenth century a nun bit another, who took such delight in it that she in turn bit another nun, until biting became a real epidemic, spreading from one convent to another.

A widespread expression of sadomasochism is flagellantism. Not only individuals but whole countries succumbed to it. It was again the Church which supported it by declaring sex a sin. This led to perversion of the sex instinct and its expression in cruelty. Self-castration flourished. Pater Damiani, Abbot of the Benedictine monastery Santa Croce, set an example of self-whipping. To justify it he recited the one hundred fiftieth psalm, which says—Praise God with tymbals. A tymbal, he reasoned, is a dried skin, ergo, who beats himself with a dried skin is praising God. The monk, Dominicus Loricatus, is reported to have excelled all other self-beaters in that monastery. During whippings he recited psalters. Despite such strenuous activities some of these monks reached an old age: Domincus became eighty-four years old, and Romualdus lived up to one hundred twenty years. However, this was probably not the consequence of the inflicted punishment. People, who could withstand such hardship, must already have had a very robust constitution. Furthermore, the absolutely undisturbed quiet life, free of sorrows for their daily bread, and security in their old age must have contributed to saving them from the nervous afflictions of the secular citizen.

In times of stress from the outside world people are inclined to compensate for it in their phantasy-life. Whole nations may be more susceptible to the influence of imagination and may be led to imitate their leaders. That explains how lashing became a fashionable activity. Even rulers subjected themselves to it. The best known examples are the following:

Henry III of Germany never wore the king's insignia before obtaining permission from a priest, after having done penitence, confession, and lashing. Henry II of England also submitted to it. Otto IV had himself lashed even shortly before his death. Louis I was called the Saint of France because at least once a week he had the priest to whom he went for confession, discipline him by lashing. The instrument used for this purpose consisted of five little iron-chains tied together; it was called 'disciplina.' He always carried it in an ivory-box tied to his belt. Sometimes he invited noblemen and children to follow his example, giving them such chains as presents. When a confessor beat him too lightly, he urged him to be more forceful.

Eventually such private lashings led to generalized sado-masochistic procedures: In Perugia a brotherhood was formed, whose members visited churches lashing themselves on their bare backs. Such activity apparently was contagious: before long not only in Italy but all over Europe such brotherhoods were seen, wandering around, clad but in trousers. They were called flagellants. Such processions even included children. Holding leather-straps, they strapped their shoulders so hard that blood was seen flowing from them. Shedding tears, they moaned and groaned, giving the impression that they saw the sufferings of Jesus with their own eyes, and begged to be forgiven. They were seen summer and winter, day and night. They were led by priests carrying banners and crosses; and only when they were exhausted did they sink down upon church-altars. All joy and music stopped at their sight. At that time a great depression spread all over Europe and such financial difficulties contributed to making people feel guilty and desperate. Life seemed a great burden when diseases began spreading over the continent. Many people were desperate and had no goal in life. Having nothing to lose anymore, they were searching for some gratification and easily gave in to the worst orgies. The flagellants were suppressed only when they became a danger for the country—not confining themselves to their exercises of penitence but using them as a pretext for committing all sorts of crimes and eventually even opposing the Church. When all order had disappeared and chaos reigned, the Pope released a Bull against them, which eventually led to erecting pyres to keep them in check.

Lorentes was the first one to describe the Spanish Inquisition; later historians confirmed his statements. Torturing and killing of individuals has occurred at all times in various countries, but torturing for three hundred years an intelligent, spirited, and capable nation, is believed to have been the cause of the political downfall of Spain. He describes that whoever had an enemy or caused the slightest suspicion, was killed through fire. Under torments innocent people often confessed, but if they did not feel guilty and did not confess to any crime, torture could go so far as to lead to mutilation and death. Nobody dared utter his individual opinion any longer; independent thinking and development of intelligence were restricted for centuries. The first great Inquisitor, Thomas de Torquemada, was famous for his bloodthirst. The whole nation was overcome by fanaticism. Charles II ignited a pyre with his own hands to burn nine Christians and eighteen Jews. The Moors were banished from the country. The Inquisitors are said to have been as cruel as they were sensual. Incarcerated females were often used sexually. Heretics must be killed by sword and fire—was the valid maxim; even children, who were but nine years old, fell victim to the Inquisition. The number of people, who were killed by sword and fire, is said to have surpassed thirty-five thousand. Over two hundred and eighty-eight thousand were imprisoned for life. An even greater number was tortured and crippled. The most intelligent and healthy individuals were extinguished, whereas the weaklings and cowards survived. This is supposed to be the reason for the regression of intellectual and cultural life in Spain. Such gruesome deeds were committed in the name of the Christian religion.

The methods of the Inquisition have been taken over by governments in our days under the name of "psychological interrogation." Such treatment has been described frequently, and as in former times, people weakened by torment and near to death often confess to crimes they never committed. Russian prisoners described how light was shone into their eyes constantly. German political prisoners described tortures they had endured; those, who survived, showed numbers which had been engraved into their flesh, and bones which had been broken by torture instruments. "Look" of April 6, 1968 describes such methods being used on Viet Cong captives. "Psychological interrogation" includes blows, shock treatment, and wet towels, and sometimes continues all night long. Solitary confinement is used in prisons in Europe and U.S.A. even on youths.

SLAVERY: Lykurgos; Egyptians; Romans; Christianity; Turkey; Tropic Choler; Belgian Congo; Nordic peoples.

Slavery represents dominance of the stronger over the weaker. It can be met with wherever peoples of different cultural development live together. The only country where slavery has never been known is China; priests never had such authority there; people of different religions were never persecuted. In the past the Chinese were more dedicated to work than to war and intellectuals were held in high esteem. There were no sumptuous buildings like pyramids; everything was created by free labour, not by slavery.

While the pyramids were built, millions of people carried heavy stones all their lives, to satisfy the vanity of rulers. They sustained mutilating injuries as they lived their abbreviated existence. It took a long time until in the melee of inhuman use of human beings a growing conscience developed and social protest brought attention to the repulsive facts of slavery.

Although the name of Lykurgos has gone into Greek history as a representative of justice, he ruled over the slaves—helots—in an inhuman manner, taking from them all rights and imposing upon them all the heavy hard work. During the height of his reign there were more slaves than free people. The institution of Krypteia served to kill the helots from time to time in order to diminish their number.

The Romans are well-known for the cruelties they committed against slaves: old or sick ones were taken to an island in the Tiber where they were starved. Plutarch describes how a reputable person like Cato rid himself of old and sick slaves. Slaves were considered a senseless burden once they could no longer do heavy work. The emperor Hadrian pierced the eyes of one of his favorite slaves. Underground prisons—"Ergastula"—are described, where slaves were incarcerated to work during the night and often even during the daytime. If one of them had committed a crime, hundreds of them were killed with him.

The Romans were accustomed to watching bloodthirsty games from childhood on. It frequently happened that a disappointed lady vented her anger on her female slaves, e.g. slaves were stung with headpins for minor misdemeanours. Chrysostomus in his "homilia" tells us of a lady, who whipped her slaves herself, tying them to a wall. Galen's mother used to bite her slaves, as Galen himself describes.

As we have seen, Christianity, at least in the beginning did nothing to abolish slavery. When new lands were discovered, immigrants were often those individuals, who did not succeed well in their native country; they had been servants themselves and were suddenly placed in the position of commanding others. The worst things happened to slaves en route to the West Indies: Squashed together on transport ships, separated from their families, exposed to the heat of the African sun, many of them died on the way. Others arrived in a state of stupor. Pretty female slaves were used to satisfy their masters. Some were whipped at the table for the enjoyment of the guests. They were cruelly punished by the overseers for slight mistakes in their work: Their nostrils were slit open, noses cut off, or eyes torn out. They lived in primitive huts, whole families together in a single room, children witnessing sexual intercourse and brutality. No wonder that they harbour resentment and insist upon the equal rights of all mankind.

In Turkey eunuchs were in great demand as slaves. Castration was practiced on twelve year old boys. In El Obeid a physician specialized in this operation. When the operation was performed by laymen a considerable number of boys did not survive.

Tropic choler is a peculiar manifestation of sadomasochism: people, who appear to have been ordinary every-day citizens in their homeland, sometimes indulge in cruelty and uncontrollable behaviour when living in the tropics. They act in an extravagant manner, often giving way to uncontrollable rage. The case of the administrator of Tschekany, French Indochina, in the territory of Quang-Tscheou-Wan, attained some publicity: He kicked people with his heel and hit them with spades. He made them drink a mixture of cognac, absinthe, and brandy to make them confess their mistakes. His favorite distraction was using a flat-iron on his victims' skin, expressing delight in the patterns thus produced. Finally he committed suicide. His suicide can be considered a reaction-formation to sadism—out of guilt feelings, leading to self-punishment. Tropic choler is a regression to infantilism: the individual, being removed from his accustomed cultural environment and suddenly finding himself in the midst of a primitive civilization, is apt to regress to the level of such an inferior civilization, falling prey to primitive sadist instincts innate in all human beings. All inhibitions imposed by higher civilization fall away; alcohol and hot climate heighten sexual desire and contribute to removing the last inhibitions. Primitive drives find unlimited gratification. The individual enjoys his absolute power over his fellow-human beings, who are helpless and have to submit absolutely to his will. Hatred celebrates orgies, until the individual destroys himself. Usually in the tropics there are no women available from one's own social or racial group. We have seen that the sexual drive becomes overpowering when it is denied normal outlet, and under such circumstances sadomasochism may become overwhelming.

In the Belgian Congo hands feet were hacked off as punishment for offenses such as laziness. The postmaster of Bikoro, questioned by a clergyman about a basket full of hands, replied that his dog had a predilection for hacked-off negro hands. Being in charge of so many slaves makes overseers feel godlike, all-powerful. They may begin to suffer from ideas of grandeur. Many a weak character, who might not have done anything unusual in his native country, can not cope with such unusual conditions in the tropics.

We have also to consider that often persons, who are extremely cruel by nature, may be attracted to service in the tropics, sometimes without even being conscious of their motivations. Hammer (65) reports such a case: A teacher had been sexually aroused already when as a boy he witnessed other children being beaten. Later he had erections when imagining a young teacher beating a boy across the buttocks. He used to masturbate with such phantasies. He liked to read tales of Indians and descriptions of soldiers running the gauntlet. Later on he indulged in undressing his brothers and beating them, rejoicing in the reddening of the buttocks. When his education was completed, he wanted to serve in the tropics where he found conditions better suited to indulging in sadist gratification.

Bond service among the nordic peoples did not differ much from slavery: Torture was customary there too. In Russia and Poland three different torture instruments were used: Knute, Batogge, and Plette. The Knute consisted of leather straps with wire fastened in the ends. The Batogge was used on the bare body of a person, who was immobilized by one person sitting upon his head, and another upon his feet. Plette was a procedure of whipping while hands and feet were tied to a plank of wood.

Females had to place their breasts upon a marble plate in order to have them beaten with rods. Famous paintings of Madame Lopuchin show how she was disfigured because she had competed with Empress Elizabeth of Russia, imitating her by wearing a rose in her hair at a court dance. The empress made her kneel on the dance-floor and in the presence of all the participants cut off the rose together with the hair, giving her a box on the ear and returning to dancing. A slight denunciation was sufficient to later deliver her to the hangman. [Stern (66)]

SADO-MASOCHISM IN LAW: legal procedures; minorities; police brutality; case histories; death penalty; a policeman's viewpoint; arrest procedures; prisons; mental hospitals; case histories.

Even after thousands of years of civilization sadism in law is still in full bloom. When civilization was in its beginning physical punishment was an efficient tool. The lower the civilization, the harder were the forms of punishment. Assyrians, Persians, and Egyptians bragged about their cruelty. Such forms of mutilation as cutting off ears, nose, eyelids, tongue, testicles or hands were practiced. Greek mythology is full of cruelty. Sophokles describes in his tragedies how Ajax whipped prisoners despite the protests of the Goddess Minerva. Draconic laws eventually became milder in Greece; also Roman law gradually became more humane. The Romans showed more respect for the human body, wherefore surgery was not highly developed in Rome. Only serious crimes were punished by castration or nailing upon a cross.

During the Middle Ages respect for the human body was lost completely. A dynasty of executioners was formed. This profession was considered unclean. Once a person had gone into it, he was excluded from contact with the community and could mix with his own kind only. Being cut off from the rest of the community and shunned by his fellowmen, the executioner had no possibility of satisfying his drives like other people. Suppression of the sex-drive led to its manifestation in other ways. Various kinds of torture were thought up by the hangmen. One of the most popular punishments was to run the gauntlet: the delinquent was forced to walk through rows of men while being beaten by them on his bare back. This form of punishment survived until recently in the marines and in military camps. Sadistic officers, who ordered it, have been depicted with lustful expressions on their faces. Great brutality is still shown in military camps and boarding schools today, but seldom is the public informed about it. The French Foreign Legion has become famous for its abuse of soldiers. The hot climate and unnatural living conditions (as in tropic choler) contribute to the spreading of sadism. The 'Krapodine' is still used. It consists in the exposure of a deserter to the African sun and to the cold night with his extremities tied together. This is similar to torture procedures customary in the middle ages. In water torture the victim was firmly tied upon a plank and water was trickled down his throat and gradually poured into his nostrils. While he tried to swallow it, he made contortions which caused the ropes by which he was tied to cut into his flesh. In rope-torture the victim was tied, pulled up to the ceiling, and suddenly let fall; eventually he was left with his limbs broken. In a modern version soldiers dangled prisoners from a plane to make them confess. Formerly in foot-torture the delinquent was tied, his feet smeared with lard and fried upon an open fire. The ladder-torture consisted in tying the victim and extending him so much that his limbs were exartriculated. Thumb-screw and boots were less dangerous but very painful, leaving the victim mutilated for life. This was recently reascertained when former inmates of German concentration camps were examined. The sexual component can hardly be overlooked when we read descriptions of citizens of annexed countries being tied by their penis to a motorcycle and forced to run after the moving vehicle; a woman-commander making lampshades of their skin; and injections of infectious material being given under the guise of scientific experimentation. People who were considered political enemies, were shot, burned, or gassed. Usually a person, sentenced to death in the Middle Ages, had at least a chance to explain and to bring witnesses. Only after he had been sentenced did the executioners gather to enjoy inflicting tortures upon the victim, who was to die anyway, by tearing out pieces of his flesh, or forcing him into strait jackets plastered with nails.

Such contraptions were recently sold to private persons

by a London auction house, as reported by the San Francisco Examiner of March 26, 1968. This auction house is known to deal mostly in "things to enchant." Although the offerings were torture instruments from the 11th century Nuremberg Castle, they were still in great demand in our "enlightened times" by private people, who wanted to "enchant" themselves or their partners: A continental buyer, who insisted on being nameless, spent four hundred eight dollars for a boat-shaped cradle with spikes in it. A torture-chair, formerly used to make women admit they were witches, went for the same price. The collection included tongue tearers, racks, thumb screws, and an iron spider designed to rip flesh out of the body with four heated or frozen talons. There were head crowns—tin plates put on the head with spikes planted and screws arranged so they could be tightened. There were shackles, iron collars, branding irons, pillories and slow-death devices. The winner of the auction was the infamous "Iron Maiden," a three hundred year old hollow, trapdoored figure, which was bought for forty-eight hundred dollars. There were also iron masks such as Dumas made famous in his novel. One was equipped with asses' ears and a candleholder, designed for the Spanish Inquisition. Another had a trumpet in the mouth, allegedly used for libelous and backbiting people. Also greatly appreciated were an iron 'mouth-opener' and a 'mouth-closer.' The whole collection brought sixteen thousand two hundred four dollars. It had been owned by Henry Walters of Baltimore, Maryland, who had got it around the turn of the century from the Earl of Shrewsbury. An auction house official related that a great number of people asked to buy the curious objects, some of which were in great demand. It was surprising "how many kinky people want such kinky things."

The phantasy of our forefathers could hardly be surpassed in finding new methods of torture. In former times impalement, breaking upon the wheel, drowning, stoning, crucifying, scalping, skinning, sawing, tearing and stamping by elephants were methods of carrying out the death penalty in many countries. The agony of death by crucifixion has recently been investigated by French physicians, who experimented with cadavers. (Dr. Jaques Bréhant Med. World News Oct. 21, 1966). He compared his experiments with similar tortures inflicted in German concentration camps. A group of his colleagues also explored the history of crucifixion, finding its probable origin to be Asia Minor. There it was adopted by Persians and Phoenicians, who also impaled, speared, stoned, strangled, drowned and burned their victims, or boiled them in oil. The French researchers conclude that crucifixion—resulting in death by asphyxiation—is one of the 'most exhausting, anguishing forms of death.' Greeks and Jews did not customarily crucify, but Romans adopted crucifixion in the third century B.C. Jesus was condemned by a Roman tribunal. In those days it was believed that crucifixion would be an effective deterrent to crime. The Romans followed precise rules and regulations. In 71 B.C. during reprisals against the slave revolt led by Spartacus, 6000 crosses are said to have lined the road from Capua to Rome. After the death of Herod, the Roman prelate Publius Quintellius Varus crucified two thousand rebellious Jews. Under Titus, whose armies besieged and captured Jerusalem, five hundred crucifixions daily were reported. Barbet's experiments showed that the victim, stiffened by tetanus, dies of asphyxia. A Czech physician substantiated this; he had observed such death by asphyxia during World War I in the Austro-German army. A horizontal beam to sit upon was at times used to prolong the agony, whereas the 'crurifagium' hastened death by breaking the victim's legs and thus preventing him from raising himself to breathe. The Romans often hastened death by flagellation. The whip had several thongs ending in lead balls. Barbet's experiments have demonstrated that when the victim is struck in the sixth intercostal space, pericardial transudate forms which is mixed with blood when the instrument reaches the heart. Cicero described crucifixion as the most cruel and horrible of all tortures.

The Russians invented a peculiar variety of torture—instilling liquid metal into the mouth. In England an unusual variety was practiced—a heated metal-pan, in which rats were enclosed, was placed upon the abdomen of the victim; trying to escape the heat but finding no exit, the rats ate themselves into the victim's bowels.

Guillotine, hanging, and fusillading have survived into our modern times. The death penalty, still customary in many States, is a remnant from barbaric usages of the Middle Ages and is bound to disappear. Galicia, Spain, Russia, and America are among the most backward countries in this respect. The death penalty by electric chair is not as humane as is generally stated: many times people survive, becoming conscious again, starting to breathe with great difficulty, and having convulsions, so that the current has to be turned on repeatedly. Already the first case in 1890 proved this—the body entered a state of tonic convulsions; after seventeen seconds the current was interrupted, the person being considered dead; after half a minute, however, the chest began to show convulsive movements, and mucus was thrown up so that the current had to be restarted. Such complications have occurred during many executions. This form of killing can hardly be justified as humane, it is even less so than former methods and in many countries people have come to the conclusion that the death penalty is not justified at all. But still in April 1968 (The Daily Californian) there were four hundred fifty men on death-row in thirty-seven states, seventy-five condemned men in California alone. An organization 'Against Legalized Murder' was founded two years ago. They state that effective counsel is often denied and that juries are not well instructed. Countries such as Australia, Austria, India, Italy, Sweden, Great Britain, and Canada have abolished the death penalty. During the eighty-ninth Congress of Correction the conclusion was reached that —"If the death penalty has any effect at all on the homicide rate, it increases it." It slows down the legal processes and makes conviction more difficult. After a well-publicized execution there is often a rash of crimes similar to that which the executed was convicted of.

The Nazis justified castration and even extermination by explaining that a person, who was mentally or physically ill, should be prevented from procreating. In ancient times the

Spartans had new-born babies, who exhibited serious birth defects, exterminated. The Germans killed individuals afflicted with relatively insignificant handicaps, like subluxation of the hip, justifying this by stating that the State could not feed such useless individuals. Families were urged to send the afflicted individuals to a camp or hospital; later they were informed that their relatives had "succumbed to an infection." When the truth filtered through the populace became indignant.

Americans, who consider themselves so progressive, till recently still took delight in killing Negroes. In Alcorn, Mississippi to 'roast a nigger' was the main attraction during celebrations. Some pretext was easily found, sometimes unjustified, e.g. he was accused of having seduced a white woman. Police and government officials were present and approved: the crowd applauded. showing themselves to be no different from their forefathers, who had assisted at the whipping and torture of criminals.

In 1957 Ku Klux Klan members seized an elderly Negro, castrated him and poured turpentine into his wound (Look, 5-3-66). A few years later they brutally flogged a retarded youngster. Usually they choose victims, who can not fight back. A subgroup, the 'wrecking boys,' are outspoken sadists—they beat their helpless victims with leather-straps and rubber hoses. In some cases it leads to the death of the victim. In 1963 they bombed a Sunday School, killing four Negro girls. The individual submits to the group morals. The group is bound together by hatred. The agitators rail against minorities such as Catholics, Jews, and Negroes. They use dynamite, bombing synagogues in Nashville, Knoxville, Atlanta and Miami. During their festivities they carry a fiery cross—symbol of Christian love.

Hatred can be projected onto individuals or groups under a pretext such as politics, religion, or race. One no longer hates for individual-egotistic reasons but for one's country or religion. A favorite scapegoat all over the world are the gypsies: There are about five million of them scattered around the world, forming a minority that has less protection and fewer civil rights than any other minority group. Hitler killed thousands of them in gas-chambers; the Soviet Union is trying to force them into labour-pools. After centuries of persecution Pope Paul VI greeted about three thousand gypsy pilgrims at their camp outside Rome. Only recently Armenians were driven into the desert by the Turks and left to perish. Millions of Nigerians were starved to death. In Vietnam even babies were shot, and whole villages destroyed.

We need not go to distant countries to ascertain that the layer of civilization is very thin. The instinct of cruelty breaks through where we least expect it: When examining initiation ceremonies practiced at American universities quite barbaric customs can be found. The new student is expected to show courage by subjecting himself to all sorts of absurd procedures. In California in 1960 a young student was made to swallow a piece of raw liver several inches long, on which he suffocated. Students are not supposed to talk about what goes on in such fraternities. Only now and then when an accident occurs does the public hear about it and become indignant. In 1967 an American pilot trainee with a background of abstinence was forced to imbibe so much alcohol during an initiation ceremony that he died. Some years ago a student was placed into a laundry-basket and rolled down the stairs; when he had broken his limbs it came to the public's attention. The San Francisco Chronicle of October 11, 1967 described an incident during the initiation ceremony at the Baylor University Campus Service Club: "John Everett Clifton, 'drowned in his own juices'," said Justice of the Peace Joe Johnson, announcing the autopsy findings. As part of the initiation Clifton had been required to drink a mixture of laxatives and garlic. "He could have drowned either on vomit," said the Judge, "or the juices of the stuff he had been given." Before he collapsed the youth had been running in place as prescribed by the initiation ceremony.

The initiation ceremonies customary in the Apache society in Arizona could not lead to such a tragic incident. They were just an endurance test: The San Francisco Examiner of March 17, 1968 describes such a ceremony as very fatiguing since

eleven year old girls had to dance starting at sunrise a monotonous up and down dancing step in one position, while being
sprinkled with 'sacred pollen' by the medicine man. They had
to perform a marathon dance, their faces showing lines of
fatigue. These physical endurance demands symbolized the
transition from girlhood to womanhood. That such ceremonies
have their origin in the sex-drive is shown by the periodic
pantyraids by fraternities into the female students' dormitories.
In Berkeley they took the girls' brassières and other underwear;
only when their behaviour became too forceful were these
occurrences described in the newspapers. Usually, however,
such events are hushed over or depicted as great exceptions.

The man in the street is not well informed concerning legal
matters and is so bewildered that he is frightened of getting
'involved' in court actions. For fear of being drawn into unpleasantness he stays away from his fellowman in distress so
that even in a common accident in the street genuine witnesses
are hard to find, whereas unsavory individuals are willing to
testify against payment. Witnesses are often disqualified merely
because they belong to a minority group—the judge asking
whether they are American citizens. Political scandals occur
periodically and people are surprised that officials in high positions—newspaper editors and even judges—have at times been
bribed. The court procedure seldom serves to bring out the
truth; a trial is not considered a scientific investigation, but
rather termed by lawyers 'an adversary proceeding in which
other adversaries are allowed to battle it out for themselves,
so long as they follow the rules of the game laid down by the
judges.' Our law is still based upon Roman law; in fact if a
lawyer, who practised in those olden times, came alive again,
he would feel quite at home in the courtroom today because
nothing much has changed and modern methods of psychology
have not yet found entrance into legal procedure. The Hon.
Thomas C. Lynch, Attorney General of California, expressed
the following opinion on May, 1 1965—observed as 'Law Day'
—blaming businessmen for flouting legal authority, he pointed
out the contempt in our society for personal rights, property
rights, and even right to life itself, declaring that citizens are

often deprived of their rights. Slavery is not just a characteristic of bygone times—it exists in our time under different names. Formerly slaves were injured, diseased, and killed in order to add to the world's goods: when the Pharaohs, intent upon the perpetuation of their images, built the pyramids, thousands of slaves sustained mutilating injuries. Through the centuries the most damaging work has been assigned to the socially unlucky, unshielded, and unguarded, who have been exposed to trauma. Child labour still persists nowadays. Minorities have no rights; peoples from countries annexed in war were treated like slaves by the Hitler Régime; they were forced to work in ammunition factories under the most unhygienic inhumane conditions, and when they became ill they were killed.

The San Francisco Chronicle of May 17, 1968 gives an account of robbery, slavery, torture and murder in Brazil, where thousands of Indians have been systematically wiped out during the past twenty years. The attorney heading the investigation states that the methods used included shooting, dynamite, poison, and induced epidemics. The motives were lust for Indian women and desire for possession of Indian land. The women were tortured and forced into prostitution. Among the participants were an Air Force Major, a former Governor and two former Cabinet Ministers. The whole Cintas-Largas tribe in the State of Mato Grosso was killed by massacre. It came to light when a hired gunman complained that he had not been paid the promised amount for shooting the tribe's chief. Dynamite was thrown from a low flying plane and those, who survived, were mowed down by machine guns. In the Beico-de Pau tribe in Mato Grosso some three hundred men, women, and children are alleged to have died from arsenic mixed in with sugar, which was given to them as a gift. Members of the Pataxo tribe in Bahia were reportedly injected with 'small pox vaccine' which brought wholesale death.

"The need for growth and change in law as opposed to stability" was the subject of a lecture given by Dr. Cox of the San Francisco Mental Health Department to graduating students of law in June 1965. He confirmed that "the legal pro-

79

fession seldom finds a revolutionary atmosphere congenial. The need for growth and change in law is evident." Lawyers were asked to tackle the problem because they should sense society's true purpose and direction.

Policemen are given too much power over life and death: In spring 1967 a thirteen year old fleeing Negro boy was shot to death by a California policeman, who only suspected him of having attempted to steal a car. People's World of July 15, 1967 renders the account of an eyewitness of police attacking a group of teenagers, who had gathered in the street, singing and playing guitars. Two policemen picked up a youngster by his shoulders and legs and suddenly dropped him upon his back. A young girl was so badly beaten that her jaw was broken. The onlooking crowd, becoming indignant at the policemen, shouted that they belonged in Germany. The officers' reply was: "they are nothing but a bunch of animals." The San Francisco Chronicle of July 19, 1967 reported that a policeman, having come across a couple of young lovers, forced them to disrobe and whip each other upon their naked buttocks. The San Francisco Chronicle of August 29, 1968 describes how Chicago policemen clubbed and gassed demonstrators, even attacking the nonparticipating newsmen and forcing them to expose their films. It was described as "police state terror," and compared to police brutality in 1936 when Chicago police shot down ten steel work strikers on a Sunday. During the recent incident so much tear gas was sprayed that the doctors giving first aid on the side walk were affected by it; even a politician, who had left his hotel room window open while taking a shower, was overcome. A politician's secretary was clubbed when going into a drug store. Even the convention delegates were manhandled. Youngsters lying on the grass in the park were also attacked. A mere observer, the well-known poet, Allen Ginsberg, was gassed. French playwright Jean Genet and novelists Terry Southern and William Burroughs were indignant.

On September 11, 1968 San Francisco newspapers reported how a policeman, being off-duty in his home, felt annoyed at some cats and just fired his gun. The bullet went through a neighbor's window, striking a lady, who was sitting at her sewing machine, in the head. The same night a police car drove past the office of the Black Panthers firing through the windows and demolishing it. The San Francisco Chronicle of March 8, 1968 reports how anger and frustration welled up as residents of Hunter's Point told their stories of police misconduct at a meeting in their neighbourhood. Police commissioners grimly listened to shocking indictments against their department: Businessmen and veterans had been kicked in their faces; a teenager had been hit with a club; people had been beaten while detained in the city jail.

In May 1968 the San Francisco Chronicle described under the headline "Cops' Built-in Sadism" the arrest of seven hundred and twenty students at Columbia University. Uncounted hundreds were clubbed and punched so that outraged citizens asked "aren't the police monstrous?"

San Francisco newspapers of November 1969 report a policeman shooting to death a man who threatened and punished his daughter in his own home; he could easily just have arrested him.

A man who tried to cash a false check, was not even questioned, but just shot to death.

A student—attempting to crack the safe in the principal's office at Sequoia Junior High School, was shot to death.

Five policemen shot to death a single drunken man, who was armed only with a meat cleaver, instead of arresting him.

Sadist individuals are attracted by certain kinds of work. Often a person, who wants to reinforce law, has himself strong criminal drives and has—more or less successfully—tried to overcompensate for them. Fighting against being overpowered by his sadist instincts, he projects them into the outside world—on to other individuals. Therefore the potential for brutality is always there. Psychologists explain that this is just what draws such individuals to police work, stressing force above reason and decency. Through the centuries students have at times rebelled. Recently a university president was horrified by the sight of teenage boys and girls being clubbed to the ground by helmeted armed policemen. A physician giving medical aid reported that fifteen policemen beat one single student. Often when the situation merely calls for firmness the police indulge in orgies of sadism. Arthur Niederhoffer, a former policeman, confirms in his book "Behind the Shield" that authoritarian personalities are attracted by police work, which in the course of time makes them even more authoritarian.

Cobb Clubb wanted to be a policeman. He was seen in family therapy. His father had committed a crime and was in jail but the children were told that he was in a hospital. Cobb hoped his father would soon come home, as he strongly identified with him. He described his mother as inconsistent. He had always been more attached to his father, whom he described as "easygoing—a nice guy" except when he was drunk: then he beat wife and children so severely that the boy still had some scars on his back. The children witnessed terrible scenes between the parents. The last and most terrible one had been caused by Cobb himself. He wished he would not have told his mother: One night upon coming home from the movies he heard his dog yelping in his sister's bedroom. He opened the door only to discover that the source of the yelping sounds was not the dog at all but rather his fifteen year old sister, who was just being deflowered by his father. He called his mother and a scene followed. The father was drunk, the sister was crying. The mother accused the father, whereupon the father beat up mother and son. There was an atmosphere of general excitement during the following days. When Cobb and a neighbour, who was one of his friends, were babysitting, Cobb indulged in mutual oral intercourse with his friend. They were discovered and the incident grossly exaggerated by the excited mother, who was still upset. "I want to be a policeman," said Cobb, "that is a clean-cut job." This would relieve him of his guilt for being instrumental in revealing his father's sexplay with his sister. He felt he had acted like a policeman and felt guilty for having brought so much unhappiness upon the family. The mother emphasized strongly that she wanted to be divorced; but Cobb could not accept that; if he could reinstate

82

the family situation as it had been previous to the incident he would be relieved of his guilt.

Over forty years ago Alfred Adler observed that it does not depend entirely upon our "free will" which kind of work we choose. Specific experiences in life lead us to prefer certain kinds of work. He described how he acquired his fundamental knowledge of psychology—upon which he based his theories of compensation of inferiority—already when a young boy, playing in the slums of Vienna with underprivileged children. He learned by observation that people with handicaps try to over-compensate for the inferiority of an organ. One particular little boy, of delicate health, used to play "dead" in fights. Children, whose parents were immigrants, were conscious of their different home environment and if teased by others were thus made to feel inferior. They refused to speak the language of their parents, pretending not to understand it, even ridiculing their parents as they were being ridiculed by their playmates.

Adler's observations can be confirmed by observing the numerous minority groups in America today. They are treated as inferior beings and therefore unable to feel pride in their unique cultural heritage. The desire to conform and not to distinguish themselves from the majority is fostered. When children in a Chinese school were asked by the teacher what they most desired for Christmas, thirty percent wanted an English name. The majority enjoys tormenting those who are "different."

Chocido, the first born son of a Japanese family, was left in the untroubled, comfortable, secure home of his grandmother when his parents immigrated to the U.S.A. She doted on him, watching his every step. She saved his life when he climbed upon a Japanese steambath. He had many playmates. As soon as his parents had settled in the U.S.A. and established financial security they sent for him. What a shock it was when he entered school to be taunted and called "dirty Jap" and made fun of, whereas before he had been wholeheartedly accepted. Furthermore he had to change his religion and was given a Christian name. He changed from being an active, bright, and inquisitive child into being self-conscious, despondent, and withdrawn.

In an environment where peoples of many different cultures live together each group should rather cultivate and even accentuate their differences and thus contribute to the richness of the country's culture. Immigrant children are more conscious than others of the reactions of people. When grown up they may have the desire to help those who are weak and downtrodden, assisting them to become adjusted to society. Children, who have been exposed to ridicule and brutality may identify with the brutal person, striving for influence and power and misusing it. When an individual shows leadership qualities without being strong enough to lead, he is often sadistically ostracized by the group. It may happen in business, politics, clubs or office. This is a well known procedure in American life; the "boss" is influenced by the group against the individual; but it has been observed to happen at all times, in all countries.

Einstein was expelled from high school because he did not use the methods taught by his arithmetic teacher, who informed his father that 'every penny spent on the further education of this boy would be thrown away—wasted.' Freud was attacked, riciduled, and finally expelled from the medical society because he used methods revolutionary for those days. A well-known surgeon had a similar experience when during his residency he used the ureter to drain the cerebrospinal fluid of hydrocephalic infants, he was ridiculed by the hospital staff and dismissed. This method was the forerunner of modern methods of drainage through plastic tubes. When Hahnemann began to apply homeopathic treatment he was so ridiculed and persecuted by the medical profession that he had to leave his established practice and flee to Paris. There he soon established a practice again and developing his methods further, became famous.

Not only individuals but whole groups are treated forcefully and unjustly, e.g. the elderly people in the USA. Although many leading statesmen and rulers of nations are at the grandfather age and show increasing capability just because of their long life experience, elderly people are usually forced to retire, deprived of their rights and treated with disregard and even brutality.

In July 1964 San Francisco newspapers brought the picture of an elderly lady, who lived in a well-kept house of her own; but, being lonely, she used to feed birds. Hostile neighbours made a denunciation to the police. Another elderly lady was forced out of her house by three policemen when an influential party wanted to acquire her property in order to erect a high rise building. When she refused to sell it she was forcefully removed. Pictures showed her being held by three husky policemen. Her arms were forced behind her back, she was made to sit on a chair in the street. The same kind of neighbours, who are disturbed by some bird-feeding, do not consider how they disturb the whole neighbourhood by loud television and unrestrained teenage 'rock and roll' parties. There are hardly any opportunities for elderly people to be gainfully employed even part-time. Their extensive experience and potential for guiding and helping the younger generation is disregarded and wasted. Great benefit might accrue and our culture might be much enriched if the law was more favourable to minority groups and unusual individuals.

An urgent reform is due in our arrest precedures. City Councilman Thomas Murphy was arrested on a drunkenness charge in Sacramento on November 7, 1967 by sheriff's deputies. He complained, "the officers treated me like a criminal." He was an attorney and arrived at the jail to bail out a client, who had been charged with drunk driving. After more than two hours he was released. He described that officers did not let him see his client and told him to 'shut up' when he attempted to identify himself. Two policemen grabbed him and forcibly led him into jail. They mugged and printed him, took off his shoes and socks and even denied him the right to make a telephone call for bail.

Quick-to-shoot-readiness led to policemen shooting each other in New York on July 10, 1968 (Examiner). Three off-duty policemen, not apparently aware who the others were, shot each other during an argument over a stalled car. The first one's car stalled. The second one was caught in the ensuing traffic jam and got out of his car to investigate. The first one reached into his pocket for his badge in order to identify himself. However the second one, fearing an attack, shot the first one in the head. A detective of the police bureau of special services, having arrived on the scene, ordered him to drop his gun and when he was not immediately obeyed shot him in the abdomen.

We say—a person is to be considered innocent until proven guilty—yet, wherever one applies for work one of the questions asked is—"have you ever been arrested?" The San Francisco Chronicle of July 7, 1968 reports an attempt by the Human Rights Commission to end intimidation by eliminating application questions relating to previous arrests. The Commissioners urged the Civil Service Commission to do away with such questions as the following which even refer to traffic violations: "Give information even though you may not have been convicted or the records were expunged. Include all moving violations and accidents, juvenile offences and non-moving traffic violations if the fine or bail was over twenty-five dollars."

Any person may become suspect and be arrested. The San Francisco Chronicle of March 8, 1968 under the headline 'Hunter's Point' describes how minority groups are often treated and to what an extent prejudice still reigns. A Negro bail bondsman was stopped several times by police without ever having anything to hold against him. Once he was even hit on the head and ear with clubs. The policeman yelled "Look, black nigger, if you don't like it, I'll blow your brains out." Another Officer said, "we get a kick out of stopping you." Recently police officers have even been given more power—in California they are now permitted to search any-one without a search warrant.

Legal and especially penal code reforms are overdue. Even though the arrested person may be able to prove his innocence he is treated like a common criminal, sharing the prison-ward facilities with the worst law-breakers. A hard-boiled delinquent may feel very comfortable when arrested since for him this is old routine. In prison he can fraternize with his old pals. The San Francisco Examiner of July 7, 1968 reports how a person, who had been in jail twenty-one years, committed a theft in order to be arrested since he was anxious to get back into jail, his rheumatism plaguing him. However, an innocent citizen, who has never been imprisoned may feel degraded and spend day and night worrying, humiliated before his friends and family, prevented from pursuing his work during the day, and sleepless at night. The duration of such imprisonment on demand can often not be foreseen since the arrested person may not immediately be able to obtain a lawyer or a place on the court calendar. The public defender, paid by the State to represent those whose financial conditions do not permit them to engage a private lawyer, may be overworked, disinterested, or unwilling to contradict the district attorney in court. A number of prisoners leave the prison in broken spirits and have to seek medical help. This explains why arrest—as practiced today—may be demoralizing, embittering, and even add disadvantageous impressions to witnesses in the ensuing court action. This opinion is shared by prominent authorities in the field of law, e.g. Dr. jur. Lowenstein explains that false confessions and untruthful evasions may be caused by arrest and sensitive people may even be driven into suicide by such demoralizing procedures.

Still in the beginning of the twentieth century every prison-warden had the power to confine an inmate up to twelve hours in a cellar where he could hardly stand erect. There was no provision for his excrements. Ensuing unsanitary conditions led to contagious diseases spreading rapidly. Careful social education, improvement of social conditions and family life, and early psychological treatment could contribute much more to decreasing crime than punishment. Medicine and Law should be better informed about each other and work together closely. At present physicians and psychologists know very little concerning the legal aspects of situations encountered in their work, e.g. marriage, divorce, adoption, artificial insemination and sterilization. Needed reforms should be made through the articulate demands of the medical profession, social welfare, and other civic groups, with the aid of spirited individuals, judges and lawyers. Instead of being treated like a leper, the arrested person should be led back to being a useful member of society again. Nowadays he is ostracized by his fellow-men, shut away, deprived of his constitutional rights and thus punished before he even has had a chance to clear his name. Not being well informed, the man in the street has the attitude—it can't happen to me. Little does he realize how easily it can happen to anybody; Anybody can be indicted—accused of any kind of crime, even though he may not have done anything other than inviting the envy or hatred of his neighbour. Although in theory according to the American Constitution a person is to be considered innocent until proven guilty, this is not so in practice. An indicted person is treated like a criminal and deprived of his freedom.

It sounds almost unbelievable that an innocent person—merely because he has no connections and not much intelligence—can be forgotten and left in an institution for years! Yet this very thing happened in a California penitentiary, where a carpenter spent several years working diligently in the prison work shop until a social worker going through his papers accidentally discovered that he had been held by mistake. He had been arrested many years ago under the suspicion of wanting to molest a child while drunk. He behaved well, worked regularly, and repeatedly tried to obtain a lawyer. His file was misplaced and he was forgotten.

Probably this is not unusual since in the same year (1968) San Francisco papers described under the headline 'A Long Wait' a similar occurrence in Mexico City: A former postal employee waited five years in prison for his trial on charges of misusing state funds, was declared innocent by a jury and set free.

Conditions in prison have been criticized by Plaettner (67) in his book "Eros in the Penitentiary." He describes masterfully how strong young men feel, crowded together in small cells, separated from their families for years at the height of their sexual potency; all their life-instincts are frustrated. Since a young wife of a prisoner can hardly be expected to remain faithful for years, both usually feel highly strung during visits. The mate is behind bars; they can not even shake hands. Sometimes the suspicious father questions the children as to the faithfulness of the mother. It is a common occurrence that the child answers what he feels the father expects, thus becoming the controller of the mother. Tears, beatings, and scenes of jealousy follow. Plaettner alludes to the influence upon the mother and her children in case she should give birth to a baby during the absence of the father. Most prisoners are impotent after a longer imprisonment, or they want to make up for the long deprivation, and general hatred sometimes leads them to infect others with venereal disease. The manifestation described as tropic choler has its equivalent in sperm choler in prisons: the lack of partners leads to perverse substitute activities, e.g. a glass is filled with bread, an opening left in the middle into which the men place their penis when the glass is passed around from hand to hand. Tattooing done under unhygienic circumstances, shaving, haircutting and showering take on sexual significance. We have seen how the frustrated sex instinct manifests itself in other ways. Plaettner describes how twelve prisoners sucked the finger of a girl, who had immersed it into her vagina previously. He shows how crude sex manifests itself when deprived of eroticism.

During the war soldiers were led into a house of ill fame and admonished to use a girl no longer than ten minutes. Subsequently the soldiers asked how many 'cows' were at their disposal. Plaettner also describes how children were used during war-time in annexed countries. The soldiers called them 'veal' and wished each other 'good appetite.' (Plaettner—"People in Cages").

The San Francisco Chronicle of July 19, 1967 reported under the headline 'Supervision by the State' that in some prisons 'nests of electronic bugs are implanted in rooms where lawyers confer with prisoners, as well as in the jail's booking room, and even in cells where prisoners spend twenty-four hours a day.' Even what they utter in dreams can be overheard. They do not have a moment's privacy. Such conditions persisted for thirteen years without the public being aware of it. Recently Assembly Speaker Jesse Unruh has taken steps to have California's laws against electronic eavesdropping tightened.

Conditions in Spain were exposed when French newspapers described the tortures French prisoners had undergone: their testicles had been squashed, fingers broken and shoulders burned. The San Francisco Chronicle of May 20, 1968 reported that political prisoners in Greek prisons are subjected to torture: One detainee was in such bad shape after being tortured that he could only crawl along the floor on his one permitted daily visit to the lavatories. His feet were swollen like semi-inflated footballs and there was a great bulge in his groin. An American Marine was recently convicted of shooting several Vietnamese prisoners.

During the inspection of the Tucker Prison Farm in Arkansas in February 20, 1967 by Governor Rockefeller conditions there were described as bizarre. Whipping prisoners with four foot straps has been sanctioned there by law, and even torturing them by electricity or old-fashioned pliers sanctioned by custom; Arkansas tolerated such procedures because the prison is self-supporting and relieves them of the responsibility of supporting it by taxes. Life at Tucker is described as a nightmare of random violence and hopelessness. There were no schools, no rehabilitation programs, no social workers, and just one doctor turning up once a week for sick call. Some prisoners were forty to sixty pounds under their normal weight; meat was served once a month; and there was one egg per man per year on Christmas Day. Yet the two State Prison farms earn two hundred thousand to four hundred thousand dollars yearly from the sale of crops and live stock. Police uncovered that food and clothing were siphoned off by wardens and trustees for illegal sale elsewhere. The men, scantily dressed, slept in bunks, jammed against each other. Newsweek's Phillipp Carter describes how everything was for sale—soft jobs inside the prison, drugs, and even a room where for a charge of fifty dolllars prostitutes or wives could be entertained by the inmates. Liquor was readily obtainable. One inmate regularly drove to a liquor store in a prison tractor while he was supposed to be checking skunk traps. Sadism prevailed: Men were beaten not only by wardens and trustees but they also beat each other. Whippings were manically brutal—one inmate received thirty lashes for overlooking some cucumbers he was supposed to pick. Others were stomped on face or abdomen for lesser offenses. Youthful inmates were beaten if they refused the advances of homosexual trustees. As a form of punishment hypodermic needles were driven under the finger nails and electrodes attached to the prisoners' toes and genitals. When the report was published, Arkansans are said to have reacted by saying—'fleshly sin deserves fleshly punishment.' At a recent State Penitentiary Board meeting the majority argued for the continued use of the strap. At the same meeting, however, the board vetoed a proposal for branding Tucker farm cattle. Such treatment, they felt, would be inhumane!

The custom of tattooing, which is widespread in army, navy, teenage circles and prisons often attracts masochists. In prisons the tattooing is often done with primitive, unhygienic means and is extremely painful, satisfying the desire to suffer. Recent tests by Yamamoto have shown that the tattooed man has 'less stable heterosexual adjustment and a stronger desire to act out; he is more impulsive, and despite his desire to show his masculinity he has difficulty in heterosexual adjustment.' The World Medical Journal Volume VII Number 2, 1965 reports that the State of New York has banned tattooing, which it calls 'a barbaric survival often associated with morbid or abnormal personality.'

In the Californian prison, Vacaville, it has been proved that inmates can be instructed in some useful and challenging work, according to their capabilities which give their lives new meaning: They read books aloud, recording them, for use in a lending library for blind people. They have thus produced a library of four million yards of tape. This represents five hundred acoustic books, many of them textbooks for blind students. Others transcribe books into Braille. Such an important activity fills them with pride so that they even offer money to extend the library. They feel that they are doing something to help other people, not just some mechanical kind of work. It often happens that they receive letters from blind people thanking them. This has led in some instances to a lasting friendship continuing even after dismissal. One inmate, when discharged, even married a blind girl.

It is to be hoped that prisons will soon be modified and conducted according to the 'open door' model principles. Inmates should be instructed in a trade according to their capability. The fight against crime should begin in the schools. The millions spent on warfare would be better spent in education.

Whereas now and then people get a glimpse of what goes on in court actions and prisons, a natural fear has prevented them from investigating conditions prevalent in mental hospitals. The former expression 'alienist'—denoting psychiatrist—illustrates how we feel, such things as mental diseases are 'alien' to us; 'it can't happen to me.' Psychological knowledge has penetrated gradually into literature, radio, television,—mass media. When the movie industry began to present topics such as mental disease people began to wake up; suddenly it dawned on them that strange things were happening right in their midst which were hushed over by neighbours and relatives. The film that attracted the most attention was 'Snake Pit.' It depicted conditions in Rockland State Hospital in New York. The general interest it awakened led to the complete modernization of that institution. The general public is now more alert; laws regarding institutions are finally being modified; some states are more progressive than others. Nevitt Sanford stated that a cruel sign that evil is being perpetrated is the referring to victims of mental disease in less than human terms. A glaring example of this hypothesis was given by the Director of Health and Welfare's rationalization of the appalling conditions at Sonoma State Hospital by referring to patients as 'having the intelligence of household pets.' "Such a statement from a man, charged with the care of these afflicted human beings, is worse than shameful," states the San Francisco Newsletter, "it is repugnant."

Whereas protest arose against electronic devices in prison cells, even less protection and privacy are given patients in mental hospitals: The San Francisco Examiner of July 16, 1968 reported that according to a new regulation of the State Department of Social Welfare social workers are required to supply computers with intimate details about the mental illness and emotional problems of their clients. The social workers even protested, feeling that the rule opens the door to wholesale invasions of privacy. The clients give such information in confidence; such information could go out to all sorts of agencies.

In California, until recently, anybody could be arrested and taken to a mental hospital against his will, without his consent, by police force, upon denunciation. The arrested person need not have committed any illegal action; it was sufficient that he be said to have behaved 'strangely.'

Unwanted children sometimes serve as a scapegoat, e.g. A teenage boy, fighting with his younger brother, jokingly threatened to kill him, seizing a knife; wanting to make up for such hostility, he went out to buy an ice cream; upon his return—to his great dismay—he was taken to the observation ward by police, who had been called by his stepfather.

A lady refused her husband entry into the house during their divorce procedure. He did not even try to enter into an amicable discussion, but had her taken to a mental hospital. Naturally she was emotionally upset, protesting arrest. Great expenditure in time and money was involved in engaging a lawyer and proving her sanity.

Our present laws are apt to disrupt the family. The children are made to suffer. The reputation of the people involved also suffers, because there is still so much prejudice against a person, who has been in a mental hospital—just as there is against a person, who has been in prison. In both cases arrest is detrimental to one's reputation. People know very little about conditions reigning in some mental hospital observation wards, otherwise they would not so easily expose young children to such an environment: In some hospitals children are on the same ward with adults, some of whom are chronic alcoholics, drug addicts, or sexual perverts. Sadistic individuals are often attracted to work as attendants on these wards. Physical punishment, confinement to a locked room, water-procedures, or being tied to the bed are methods still frequently used, which have been taken over from the Middle Ages.

The hospital attendant, Domenico, had formerly been a champion boxer. Because of this, he was used by the hospital to deal with newly arrived patients. He took delight in slapping patients under the shower, especially young boys, since he had homosexual inclinations.

The public still looks up in awe to members of the medical profession; it is not aware that the psychiatrist in charge of the observation ward is often cooperative in having an unwanted member of the family committed. This is often a lucrative side-line for him. The present commitment-procedures sometimes take the form of witch-hunting; the patient being hunted by his own family, for various reasons: he may be used as a scapegoat, or bring substantial financial or material gain to the family. Lawyers and judges are often cooperative, sometimes out of ignorance. Such commitment procedures take place once a week on the observation wards of some State Hospitals. Heart-breaking scenes can be witnessed: sobbing wives being committed by their husbands as a punishment for having been unfaithful; husbands being committed by unloving wives, who want to appropriate their spouse's possessions.

A lady attempted to have her husband committed because he was too old to be gainfully employed and thus a burden to her. He was her third husband. She had married him in order to have financial security. Now, however, he was too old and she felt that her workload as a housewife would lessen if she were to live in his house alone. With the cooperation of the ward psychiatrist she established the diagnosis of Alzheimer's disease.

The judge conducting such procedures does not know the patient. He dedicates an average of ten minutes to each patient. He relies on the opinion of the ward psychiatrist, at times even the young resident, often hardly glancing at the case history. Furthermore he is not familiar with medical terminology. In many places a judge can commit a person if two doctors agree that he is mentally

94

ill. They do not even have to be psychiatrists. The doctors often conduct superficial examinations, sometimes lasting but a few minutes. It is possible that a person may be upset or belligerent because he has been brought in against his will. The judge is put in the awkward position of having to either question or accept the professional judgement of the doctors. In the great majority of cases he has no alternative but to accept it. How could he put someone back on the street when the doctors say he is mentally ill! Seymour Shubin in the SK&F Psychiatric Reporter of January 1968 states that the average commitment hearing in California takes less than five minutes. Mental Health Association members sitting in on those hearings felt that in many cases outpatient treament would have been sufficient. Only about ten percent of these patients were considered violent or dangerous to themselves; yet eighty-three percent of State Hospital patients, most of them poor, were committed involuntarily. A person, who has been committed, can lose sixteen legal rights—seven more than a convicted felon. Some of these are lost automatically: the right to engage in any state-licensed business or profession, to hold public office, to vote. Even when he appeals the temporary loss of rights adds to the ordeal and stigma of being mentally ill.

Conditions in California will greatly improve when the new Lanterman-Petris-Short Act goes into effect. Then commitment can no longer be the result of a family fight as happened recently:

A young Australian girl, while traveling in America, was accommodated in the home of a member of the consulate. Feeling helpless and somewhat lonely in the new country, she attached herself to her host, the consular official. His wife, seeing them in an embrace, became so jealous that she summoned the family-doctor, a relative of hers. She said: "the girl must be crazy if she acted like that, 'biting the hand that fed her.'" The doctor was instrumental in committing the girl, who was later sent back to her native country. Her parents, being puzzled by her introverted, depressed behaviour which the exuberant young girl had never exhibited before, had her subjected to a lobotomy, which at that time was relatively new in Australia. Whereas she had been unusually brilliant, even graduating summa cum laude from college and winning a gold medal, she was now barely able to cope with simple household duties and became docile, downtrodden and disinterested. Her parents married her off to a much older man.

Under the new law a confined person will have the right to refuse shock treatment or lobotomy. He will be permitted to make and receive telephone calls which was forbidden til recently.

A civil servant had his wife committed, stating that she was potentially dangerous. She was considerably younger than he and had married him for financial reasons. Feeling repelled by his unusual sex practices she wanted a divorce. One morning when she had just gotten up she was standing by the window and enjoying the beautiful morning when she noticed a car driving up. She thought this unusual at such an early hour. When she saw her husband at the garden entrance she thought everything was alright, these men must be his business acquaintances. However, they were policemen summoned by her husband to take her to a mental hospital. Under these circumstances it was natural that she fought violently and was given a sedative injection. Not being permitted to make any telephone calls, she was unable to obtain a lawyer. Her husband, having powerful political connections, arranged her commitment.

The patient in such a situation is helpless and distraught; sometimes he does not even understand the procedure. In some hospitals he is not even permitted to dress for the court procedure but is made to appear before the judge in his striped hospital gown. This is a humiliating experience. Only a small percentage of patients are sufficiently educated to know that they have the right to obtain a private lawyer. A lawyer is not necessarily a person, who acts in accordance with high moral and ethical standards:

A well-known attorney had his rich wife committed and has been keeping her in a mental hospital for many years. When an unsuspecting idealistic young psychiatrist offered to treat her, he became very apprehensive and refused. Being threatened and extorted by the nurse, who had assisted him to have his wife committed, he had to share his home with the nurse. Subsequently his young son became fearful and hostile and eventually left the house to live elsewhere. The attorney, at first feeling exuberant and enjoying the feeling of power his wife's large fortune gave him, investing it in real estate, was finally weighed down by guilt and tormented by his son's increased hostility. He assumed a masochistic attitude towards the nurse, submitting completely to her domination. Eventually he became depressed and developed physical symptoms such as diarrhea, polyuria and headache. Finally seeing no way out of this desperate situation, he committed suicide.

In some cases confinement in a mental hospital is used as a reason for the annulment of a marriage—to be free of marriage shackles, furthermore even allowing for revenge and dispossession.

Only recently have the shameful conditions in California hospitals come to the knowledge of the public and are commitment procedures being changed. Various American psychologist organizations courageously criticized conditions prevailing in mental hospitals and approached Mental Health Planning Committees.

In some states, e.g. N. Carolina, persons admitted to state mental hospitals lose their right to vote, to drive a car and to transact business. They regain these rights only after official discharge. Psychotropic drugs have been conducive to reducing the number of necessary commitments. Most psychiatrists are convinced that chemical and physical approaches are capable of dealing with the symptoms, whereas psychodynamic methods of therapy help the mentally disturbed patient to experience maturation and growth of personality. In mental hospitals—as in prisons—the 'open door' institutions have been shown to be superior. The legal procedures pertaining to commitment are undergoing change. Unnecessary involuntary detention should be avoided and prompt help with a minimum of legal disability and stigma should be provided.

Just as in prisons so it happens also in mental hospitals that people endowed with a certain quantity of masochism, or discouraged in life, enjoy being cared for, even at the price of freedom.

A migrant worker returned to the hospital each winter with a myriad of complaints, whereas during the warm season he returned to his work. He had been brought up by a domineering aunt, hated all females, and did not want to return to his homeland. He had homosexual activities even on the hospital ward where he stayed during winter in order to save his small earnings.

A young man, who had grown up in institutions returned to the hospital whenever he lost his job, often just to enjoy regular meals for a little while until he had gathered enough courage to face life again.

Another man worked in the coal mines. During a quarrel over a girl he stabbed his rival and was arrested. Older prisoners instructed him in simulating epileptic fits. Thereupon he was transferred to a mental hospital. Experienced inmates advised him to 'cook up some mental symptoms,' in order to remain at the hospital. Consequently he heard voices stating they 'would make him clean,' and saw females on the ceiling of his room at night.

Among those, who consider it an advantage to be institutionalized, there is the category of patients, who want to be restrained. Then they can feel protected against their own violence which may be directed outward against others or inward against themselves; they can feel at peace and secure.

Furia repeatedly requested that she be put in a strait jacket. Only then could she feel secure against her own violent impulses. She had been forced to look after her younger stepbrother. Filled with murderous hatred against him, she had to fight in herself the impulse to kill him. Believing in the 'healing power of positive faith—and love—aspects,' she married a minister, hoping to be helped by such a religious husband to restrict her murderous impulses. Being cool, reserved, and distant he was unable to satisfy his temperamental wife. When she gave birth to a baby-boy with a cleft palate, she blamed herself, believing that she had caused it by having harboured death wishes against the unborn baby. She developed a post-partum psychosis, which brought her to the hospital. She hated even her husband, who had failed to envelop her in the security of love and religion.

A teenage boy, Luke, hated his alcoholic father and his step-mother, both of whom were very strict. Once, while intoxi-cated, the father threw Luke down the stairs. The stepmother considered him a burden and brought him up with cruelty. One of her favorite punishments was to place him into a gyrating washing-machine. He reacted with fear and hatred. Having been taught in school that hatred is wrong, he tried to repress it. Therefore it found expression in unusual activities, e.g. he felt jealous of peacefully growing plants and therefore cut down all the bushes and flowers in the frontyard. He pro-tected himself against his hatred with masochism. He asked his playmates to bind him so tightly that he would be unable to move, and to abandon him at the beach in such a condition. When he felt all alone, afraid to be left there even at night, exposed to the incoming flood, unable to free himself, he ex-perienced a state of bliss which led to orgasm. Being tied so fast that he couldn't even move, made him feel safe against his own murderous drives.

SADO-MASOCHISM IN MEDICINE: treatment of mentally ill in the past and the present; torture; gyrators; convulsions; shock; black market in corpses; cruel surgeons and dentists; unethical procedures; experimentation; harmful drugs; case histories; necrophilia; paramedical personnel; hypnosis; tranquillizers; self-experimentation.

As we have seen choice of profession may depend principally on life-experiences and character. The student's main goal is usually that of acquiring skill and knowledge, and he is but little concerned with the ethical obligations to be maintained by a professional person throughout his life. Medicine should not only be a science but also an art; and for the physician it should be a way of life. The Declaration of Geneva, trying to maintain the honour and noble tradition of the medical profession introduced by Hippocrates, contains passages which are in conformity with the basic ethical principle—do unto others as you would have others do unto you. In many countries, the physician taking the oath of Hippocrates at graduation, solemnly pledged to consecrate his life to the service of humanity and not to permit considerations of religion, nationality, race, party politics, or social standing to intervene between his duty and his patient. He promised to maintain the utmost respect for human life, even under threat; and never to use his medical knowledge contrary to the laws of humanity. This appeal to honour and to charity has ennobled the profession even in its darkest hours. A physician, having power over his fellow human-beings, may use it as prescribed by the Declaration of Geneva, but also to satisfy sadistic inclinations.

Sadomasochism in medicine can be traced through the history of all times. Superstition influenced the healing arts for centuries. Mentally ill persons were considered possessed by the devil and locked up in cribs. Still nowadays violent patients are sometimes strapped to their beds.

Modern strait jackets seem to be a remnant from former times, although tranquillizers and sleeping pills are rapidly displacing them. The old-fashioned "Gyrator" consisted of a box, which made a hundred turns per minute, while the patient was inside it. It was supposed to calm the patient. Recently it has again been manufactured and was bought by the director of a mental health clinic,—not as a museum-piece— but because he had let himself be convinced that it would exercise the patient, use up his energy, and thus make the patient feel weak and docile. Then the clinic would be able to reduce the amount of medications and the number of nursing personnel required. Patients suffering from convulsions were beaten during the Dark Middle Ages in the belief that this would cure them. However, they are still beaten nowadays by attendants, whose sadism drives them to work in such institutions where they can exploit the helplessness of their victims.

Clara, a young manic-depressive, required repeated short hospitalizations during her manic phases. When her mother brought her home after one of these, she discovered that Clara was covered with bruises. In response to her enquiry the hospital director admitted that patients are frequently beaten by the attendants.

Doctors usually do not object to such treatment by the nursing personnel because they want to maintain a friendly relationship with the staff.

We are not amazed to read about court actions following such occurrences as in the case of Dr. Kuelz, who was hospitalized in 1967 in the San Francisco General Hospital for diabetes. He described how cruelly he was treated by young residents; one of them, apparently having sadistic inclinations, urinated upon his bedclothes. Dr. Kuelz displayed unusual courage in exposing such conditions and not being afraid of publicity. Usually such occurrences are hushed over. In a home for elderly people the director had difficulty finding orderlies; most of them did not want work in a rural environment. Most of them

101

CARL A. RUDISILL LIBRARY
LENOIR RHYNE COLLEGE

drank heavily, especially on weekends, and frequently burnt patients when giving them a bath, repeatedly even breaking their ankles. Especially women patients were often covered with bruises, but were afraid to denounce orderlies, anticipating revenge.

For a long time physicians thought that diseases were punishments inflicted by God. Physicians considered themselves moralists and priests, openly indulging in brutality. Still nowadays humaneness is not always the basis of their profession. Formerly in the famous Salpetrière and Bicêtre hospitals all patients afflicted with Syphilis admitted they were cruelly whipped. Both in the Bicêtre and in St. Médard near Paris patients were laid in chains. Still nowadays even in American hospitals patients often arrive in handcuffs. In the eighteenth century, when the famous Parisian psychiatrist Philippe Pinel wanted to free patients from being martyred and asked permission to unchain those under his care, proposing to make them work, the Commissioner of Hospitals exclaimed: "Are you crazy yourself, wanting to liberate these ferocious beasts?"

As the interest in anatomy increased in the beginning of the nineteenth century, a critical shortage of dead bodies developed. The black market in corpses flourished. They were even robbed out of graves. The case of William Hare has become famous. He ran a cheap rooming house in Edinburgh. When his roomers died, he cashed in their bodies for back rent, selling them to Dr. Knox for dissection. When they did not die fast enough, he smothered them by sitting on their heads, assisted by his friend Burke. Only when well-known persons were found in the Anatomy did a scandal develop.

Even such a famous scientist as Sir John Hunter did not refrain from taking recourse to extreme measures when in quest of an unusual skeleton: When the Irish giant, O'Brien, who was eight feet four inches tall, refused to promise him his body, he had him shadowed. In vain the desperate giant changed lodgings repeatedly. Despite the giant's numerous precautions, Sir John Hunter succeeded in obtaining his body by intoxicating and bribing one of his servants. In those days there was a widespread prejudice against dissection. When in the pursuit of specimens Hunter did not refrain from threatening with disease and even murder when he met with resistance.

Medicine was assisted by the church when the Black Plague struck congested cities in the Middle Ages. When Henry IV was excommunicated, he was forbidden to take hot baths. Isabella of Spain took a vow not to change her chemise for three years. A guest was always highly honoured when offered a bath. Lepers were compelled to wear special shoes and burial shrouds, to lie in a coffin before the altar, and be declared legally dead by the priest. From that day the leper had to beg alms to support himself. He was often accused of polluting wells and threatened with death. In this respect medicine has made progress: In some countries people afflicted with leprosy mix freely with the community; in others they are confined to leprosariums where they live in their own houses, selecting occupations according to their capacity. (Hawaii, Sicily)

It is instructive to compare medical procedures used in former times with modern methods of treatment. Thus we may convince ourselves that one of their conspicuous components is sadism. Mental patients, not being able to defend their interests, have always been abused: In former times they were exposed to hunger and thirst, being thrown into water; withdrawal of sleep, sneezing and vomiting cures, artificially maintained suppuration, burning of moxae (little cotton balls) on the skin, whipping with stinging nettles, brushing the soles of the feet, and tickling with caterpillars. Reil surpassed his sadistic colleagues in originality by recommending that the patient be placed in a container of eels. People, who were so withdrawn that they were indifferent to food and drink, were exposed to such procedures as induced vomiting, immersion into cold water or permanent drop-bath, which consisted in immobilizing a patient in a strait jacket under a tap from which drops of cold water dripped upon his head at regular intervals. Mice were placed upon the abdomen under a glass. The soles of the patient's feet were smeared with salt and goats induced to lick it. If all these procedures had not improved the condition and the patient had not yet passed away, scabies was induced because the constant itch was supposed to cure catatonics. Reil also recommended that the asylum be located near a lake or river in order that the patients might be thrown into the water unexpectedly. He warned that it would not help if—out of fear that they might die—they were saved too soon. He was convinced that procedures such as those he recommended would bring the patient close to death. This old idea is still the basis for some current methods of therapy, such as the artificial induction of convulsions or coma: It has been postulated that in the application of shock treatment (cardiazol, metrazol—Meduna; insulin—Sakel; electric—Cerletti and Bini) the victim, being close to death, struggles with all his might for life; and many times the life instincts win—he has amnesia for recent occurrences which may have led to escape into insanity—a new life pattern is formed. Catastrophes occur sometimes but are usually hushed over: People sometimes break their bones during convulsions.

The bank-manager Errando became depressed after a financial catastrophe. Despite his vehement objections, his wife, a well-known contemporary woman-doctor, insisted that he have shock treatment. During the convulsions he broke both legs. As a consequence of such traumatic experiences he became paranoid.

Lorna, an eighteen year old only child, became melancholic after an unhappy love-affair. Her parents were delighted when she picked up strength and put on weight during her course of insulin-shock therapy. However, after she awakened from one of her treatments, she was found to have developed a hemiparesis.

Only fifty years ago barbers still pulled teeth in rural communities where dentists were not available; anesthesia and sterility were seldom used even by real dentists. This has been described by Thomas Mann in the "Buddenbrooks" and by Goethe in his letters to his wife Christiane. Simple villagers and farmers considered the removal of teeth the best remedy when afflicted with a toothache. Barbers acquired skill through practice. Is it very different today? The general public is but poorly informed about the often harmful practices of credit dentists.

Bobby, the elevator-boy, had had such a terrible toothache already for several days. He was walking down the street hanging his head. When crossing the street he looked up and a big sign—"Credit Dentist Dr. Castro" suddenly caught his eye. "That must be a sign of Fate," he thought and ran up the stairs. The dentist suggested that pulling the tooth would be painless and the most effective and quickest cure. What a letdown it was when everybody teased him about his missing front tooth and asked him whether he had been in a fight. He returned to the dentist and was flabbergasted to learn how expensive a single tooth would be. Dr. Castro told him it would only cost a few dollars more per month to have all his teeth pulled and a complete set of dentures made. Then he would never need any further dental treatment for the rest of his life. Bobby thought "How wonderful never to have to go to the dentist again," and following the dentist's advice had all his completely healthy teeth pulled.

Dr. Alden was in psychotherapy because he could find no normal outlet for his sexual drive. Not being attracted by women from his own social group, he had married a very simple unintelligent girl from one of the lowest socioeconomic groups. She longed to have a child. Since he was unable to go through with intercourse he agreed to her having a baby by artificial insemination.

Already in chidhood he had felt inferior to other boys. He grew up in a rural setting; being repeatedly afflicted with severe ringworm infections of the scalp, he had to undergo many painful treatments and to keep his bandaged head covered with a cap. He was already completely bald in his late teens. In addition a severe mumps infection caused him to be sterile. During his childhood when meeting visitors, he did not give a friendly greeting and take off his cap like the other boys did because he was ashamed of his bandaged head. When admonished he began to cry. When grown up he felt different from other men and could make no friendly contact with either men or women. Tormenting women gave him a feeling of strength and superiority. This determined the choice of his profession. He specialized in endodontics because he particularly enjoyed using sharp pointed instruments in root canal treatment. Reducing young attractive women to a state of abject terror caused him to experience sexual excitement. For hours after having sent them home, he was in a state of exaltation, imagining how they were continuing to suffer, because he had taken special care to expose the nerves of the treated teeth. He arranged to be unavailable for several hours and only when his patients returned to his office late in the evening did he condescendingly relieve their pain.

Only seldom has the doctor been held responsible for the results of his treatment. The Babylonians (2000 B.C.) had a scale of fees fixed by law, based on the patient's ability to pay and on the seriousness of the case. However, payment was made only upon recovery and—what was worse—the doctor was punished for failure, again according to the scale, e.g. loss of a nobleman's right arm meant loss of the doctor's right hand; death of a slave meant replacement by a new slave.

In the sixteenth century under the Persian Safavid dynasty the use of surgery for punishment developed, for practically all Persian rulers were cruel and bloodthirsty; amputation, castration, and blinding—often of relatives who might be rivals—were commonplace. Nor was the surgeon's life free from anxiety; his master was quite capable of having him put to death.

In 1832 Delpech, one of the founders of orthopaedics, was killed by one of his disgruntled patients. In some countries the laws pertaining to medical practice are still in favour of the patient (Medical World Vol. XIII No. 6 Nov./Dec. 1966).

Maitre Jean Mignon states that article sixty-three of the French Penal Code of 1945 made it obligatory for a doctor to aid any person in danger. The punishment for noncompliance was increased in 1954. The "Daily Press and Television News" carried pictures of a Dr. Colin handcuffed between two policemen. In November 1964 a youngster was stabbed in the femoral artery in Nancy. Dr. Colin, called at four o'clock in the morning, tried in vain to get an ambulance and undertook nothing further. He was arrested the next day and in June 1965 condemned to four months' imprisonment and a thousand francs fine. On appeal he was not imprisoned but the fine was raised to five thousand francs.

If protective rules were enforced, it could not happen, that an obstetrician instructs the nurse to hold back the head of a baby ready to be born until he can appear and complete the delivery at his leisure and convenience. This procedure has often resulted in brain damage. Nicholson and Eastman (Current Medical Digest P.520 April 1966) warn against this evil practice, describing the case of a mother who gave birth to two normal children, but then delivered two others who developed cerebral palsy because their heads had been held back until the arrival of the obstetrician.

The World Medical Journal Vol. XIII # 6 Dec. '66 is dedicated to the subject of ethics and medical research. It condemns human experimentation, referring to the article of Beecher in the New England Journal of Medicine of June 16, 1966. Part of the argument concerns the 'informed consent' of patients—or experimental subjects. Beecher explains that grave consequences may be suffered by the person who subjects himself to such experimentation. He suggests that out of one hundred studies a dozen seem to be unethical, describing that in some cases of serious illness a known effective treatment was withheld. Often harmful drugs are given, e.g. one drug was thought to interfere with liver function whereupon the children treated with it were subjected to biopsy. Beecher describes tragedies caused by such experiments, stating that procedures such as cardiac catheterization, liver biopsy, and some forms of anaethesia used carry a high mortality rate. This is sometimes overlooked. The mortality rate for cardiac catheterization is $1/1000$ where the right side of the heart is involved, $5/1000$ when the left side is involved, while for liver biopsy it is $3/1000$. He pointed out that ordinarily patients would not be inclined to risk their health or their life for the sake of science. The Medical News of February 27, 1967 reported that five hundred or more mentally retarded children at Willowbrook State Hospital were injected with live hepatitis virus in a research program and used as guinea pigs. When such risks are taken, it can be assumed that 'informed consent' has not been obtained. When a patient signs a consent form, he is usually unaware of research being done. He is often in acute distress or has to sign a flurry of papers without understanding them.

The scandal of unexplored and harmful drugs being used by doctors has even reached our daily newspapers. Reports deal not only with single instances such as thalidomide resulting in the birth of deformed babies, but also describe the well-known practice of drug companies who offer 'research grants' sometimes amounting to thousands of dollars to physicians, who agree to test new drugs on their patients.

Indeed we have come a long way from the time when Hippocrates laid down guiding principles for the medical profession and defined the aims of medicine. In those days a physician was a highly esteemed individual, because his goal was to help his fellow human beings. Nowadays medicine has been degraded to a mere business, and the individual has been degraded to a mere guinea pig. Dr. Maurice H. Pappworth documented numerous cases of human experimentation in which— he believes—the risk outweighed the possible benefits. He states that patients were subjected to mental and physical stress in no way related to the treatment of their disease. In some cases recovery was deliberately retarded in order to allow the investigation to continue. He cites examples of children, suffering from acne vulgaris, who were given an experimental antibiotic; eight children subsequently developed severe liver damage. He points out that of all the patients who had received heart transplants none had survived for any length of time. The kidney transplant expert, Dr. John S. Najarian, proposed that a policy setting commission be set up. "Whether or not any proposed experiment is legally and ethically justifiable must never be the sole opinion and decision of the experimenter himself or his team." Only in this way, he feels, can "the zeal to extend the frontiers of medical knowledge" be controlled. Otherwise patients will be used just as guinea pigs (Medical World News April, 1968).

William Barry-Furlong courageously discussed the question whether people should be subjected to medical experiments without their prior knowledge and consent. Already a few years ago live cancer cells were injected subcutaneously at the Chronic Disease Hospital in Brooklyn. The patients had been told that it was 'an immunity test.' The truth was deliberately withheld; there was a significant risk. Furthermore, nineteen of the twenty-two subjects did not even have cancer, but suffered from other ailments. Only when an attorney was consulted, was it revealed that in other hospitals two hundred and seventy-five patients had been subjected to various experiments. Three hundred inmates of the Ohio State Penitentiary had been used as guinea pigs. Five hundred cases, including several children, were reported by British physicians. Dr. Beecher cited twenty-five cases from the charity ward in the Massachusetts General Hospital, calling them martyrs. 'Research' was also performed upon five hundred eighty-five servicemen at the Warren Airforce Base in Wyoming, a number of them being crippled for life by chronic disease.

How far have doctors departed from the aims and ideals of their profession! The desire for power, money, or fame now all too frequently rules their actions. Formerly the Society for the Prevention of Cruelty to Animals objected to ruthless and painful animal experimentation; nowadays the State consents to human beings being used as laboratory animals. In the New Physician a student—whose name was withheld—recommended that in the future illegitimate children should be caged and used as guinea pigs in laboratories. College students and prison inmates are made to "volunteer" in the hope of gaining better conditions in their routine life. When a person is given responsibility he has the opportunity to abuse it. A general ethical code can support, but not substitute—for the conscience of the individual.

Surgery can be considered a refined and fruitful sublimation of sadism. Sometimes surgeons are under a compulsion to cut: they are obsessed with removing certain organs, e.g. thyroid, ovaries; showing repetitious behaviour. Often they do not prepare the patient. Children are frequently treated cruelly, sometimes not sufficiently anesthetized. Only recently twenty-six small children were thymectomized, the surgeons pointing out that the thymus did not fulfill any function. Barry Furlong has objected, arguing that the thymus is essential for normal growth, and that its removal was not necessary.

A century ago Lister advised: A good practical surgeon is successful only if he does the right operation well, at the right time, and if he knows how to take care of his patient intelligently afterwards. If he does the wrong operation at the wrong time and does not understand the intricacies of the care of his patient before and after operation, then his being merely a good operator is of no value; too many of his patients will die.

The emotional impact of hospitalization, especially upon young children, is underestimated. Periodical survey of heart operated children has shown that even years after recovery they reacted with fear and negativism to all medical personnel. Most of the children—as reaction formation to having been helplessly exposed to excessive suffering—had developed sadomasochistic character traits.

Most surgeons have developed callousness; overenthused surgeons remove everything that can possibly be removed without endangering life, e.g. tonsils, appendix, gall bladder, prostate, and thyroid. It can be considered a desire to mutilate or castrate.

Menninger has described the desire of masochistic patients to be operated upon, as addiction to surgery. Such masochists regard the surgeon as a father-figure, cruel, firm, omnipotent. Many famous surgeons, e.g. Sauerbruch, are known to have been coarse and ruthless. A well known proctologist became highly excited when introducing a sigmoidoscope into the rectum of young elegant females. He was unable to perform ordinary sexual intercourse. Masochistic patients think of a hospital as a restful place where one gets attention from young nurses, quiet rest, relief from the necessity of work, attention and pity, and mothering by parent-substitutes; furthermore, on the ward they can satisfy exhibitionistic tendencies. Sometimes an operation is a kind of self-castration; financial disaster, venereal disease, homosexuality, and impotence may represent the disguised desire to be castrated. Masochism can even mean a triumph of life instincts over death instincts: he would rather sacrifice part of his body than be dead. Accidents, as Menninger points out, may be caused to oneself by guilt feelings, or to others by unconscious antipathy.

Surgeons do not often confess that operating gives them gratification. Experience shows that with the exception of a few, who have selected this speciality because of family tradition, early childhood experiences determine their choice:

A well-known surgeon, chairman of the department, confirmed this. His childhood was extremely unhappy: His father, a ruthless businessman, had little time for his family and no interest in his boy; the only occasions when he gave him any attention being when he reprimanded or punished him. The mother helped her husband in the business. The household was run by an old maid aunt, who was described by him as 'sour-puss.' Having been disappointed by men, and being dependent upon her brother-in-law, she could act out her accumulated hostility only upon the helpless boy. Already during his medical studies, he decided upon surgery: the cutting and destroying of tissues, having the patient completely under his power, represented a gratifying situation. He consciously hated his father so much that—when called to his deathbed, he left without even wanting to see him when it turned out that the illness was not fatal. He became a very successful surgeon.

The surgeon, Professor Aragona, had been an adopted child. He described how he had always felt like an outsider, never having experienced emotional closeness with another human being during his entire childhood. During operations he became sexually excited. He preferred to perform minor surgical procedures without anesthesia, becoming greatly excited upon hearing the patient scream. On these occasions he perspired so profusely that afterwards he had to take a shower. Then he used transparent nail polish, perfumed himself, and donned a cream-coloured dressing-gown. Thus attired he pulled young attractive female students into empty rooms on the ward, attempting to seduce them.

Another surgeon, Professor Cermotti, usually appeared friendly and good-natured and was much admired. During operations he changed completely: Perspiration appeared on his forehead, he was transported into a state of extreme excitement—almost frenzy; his movements became abrupt; he shouted at nurses and assistants, his excitement mounting so that during certain operations he even developed a fever. After the operation he felt completely exhausted and sometimes—to his own surprise—discovered that he had had an ejaculation. He enjoyed the reputation of being a very skillful, excellent surgeon. Apparently he had sublimated his destructive sadism into something positive, helpful, and constructive. His brother, also endowed with an unusual amount of sadomasochism, sublimated it by becoming a member of the priesthood in the Vatican. When they were but in their infancy their mother had died. They grew up without tender loving care under the dominance of a stern, cool housekeeper. Later they were placed in a strict catholic boarding school, where they were exposed to cruelty and homosexual approaches.

Ilnikov, a pathologist at a famed institution seemed to be a dedicated scientist, above every situation; he had published a number of papers and his laboratory had such unusual specimens that he was visited by colleagues from other parts of the country. Knowing him but socially, one would have presumed that he was in a harmonious state of mind, that he came from a happy family, and that he had attained gratification and happiness. However, he was most unhappy in his private and professional life despite his outward success. His desire to be in graveyards turned out to represent an expression of repressed revenge-phantasies. As a child he harboured death-wishes against his younger sister, who was preferred by his mother. Being disappointed by his mother, he devalued women in general. In revenge for having to put up with disregard, he destroyed all his own and his sister's toys. When this envied sister died, he felt guilty, as if he had caused her death. Once a dead body was washed up on the river-bank near their house. Subsequently the death-wishes heretofore subconsciously maintained against both mother and sister, became conscious; his guilt increased and he expected retaliation. He became a pathologist because—as he expressed it—'dead bodies can not fight back;' with them he felt safe. He had erections and at times ejaculations, while dissecting.

Necrophilia is not as rare as one might assume: Lyon describes in 'Le Vampirisme' sadistic sex acts performed upon women in churchyards. The men performing them, suffered from headaches and epileptic fits before committing the acts.

Several medical specialties offer an excellent possibility to sublimate those drives which are not in harmony with the demands of civilization. At first glance one would assume that an obstetrician would be fond of women and babies.

In the case of Dr. Freeman his work was an outlet for his hatred. On the surface he was smooth and amiable. He had become director of the university's department of gynecology at a relatively young age. It was assumed that his scientific interests and heavy work load had prevented him from marrying; that he dedicated himself completely to his profession. The lack of time was held responsible for his arrogant attitude towards women. However, he did not feel at ease with men either, having no close friends and keeping his colleagues at a distance.

Wishing to protect his reputation, he underwent psychotherapy while on a sabbatical leave in a distant country. He described the deprivation he had suffered during his formative years. His father had been director of the same department and wanted the son to follow in his footsteps. His father believed the home-atmosphere to be inappropriate for the development of his son's character and personality, because his wife favoured a younger son, who was of inferior intelligence. Therefore the boy was sent to spend his childhood in a foster-home. The foster-father was a minister of a different religion, stern and unapproachable. Although he made an effort to treat the boy the same way as he treated his own children, the boy always felt like an outsider—not like a member of the family. The minister's real children considered the boy inferior. When they shared snacks they only gave him the left-overs. He resented that his father had sent him away and blamed his mother for having consented. He felt he had been turned out

113

of the home. He did not hate his brother, whom he considered too inferior. After graduation he was glad to be on his own and embarked upon his career. Upon his father's death he succeeded to his position.

He considered the women as 'material' and despised them. "All his time was taken up by his work"—was his excuse for not mixing with his colleagues, whom he thought he should keep at arm's length. Yet he had a constant longing for emotional contact with another human being. Eventually he adopted a little girl, whose mother had died of cancer. When he used to make house-calls, the little girl had often opened him the entrance-door, and she had always smiled and been so friendly and trusting. Since she had no relatives, she was completely dependent on him. In this relationship he need have no mistrust or fear. He brought her up in his luxurious home. As she grew up, a tender, almost amorous relationship developed between them. When she began to attend parties, he was jealous of her suitors. Trying to isolate her, he took her on vacations, but wherever they went, she attracted the attention of men and was asked to dance. She told him particularly about one of her dance partners, whom she described as an attractive, intelligent, friendly medical student. At an after-dinner dance in the hotel this young man again danced with her. Jealousy welled up in Dr. Freeman; unable to control himself, he jumped on the dance-floor and threw himself upon the dance partner, attacking him. Tears and scenes followed, which made him decide upon psychotherapy.

Unusual or extreme methods of treatment are furthered not only by strong sadistic drives in the doctor but also by masochistic tendencies in the patient. Doctors often recur to some methods which remind us of medieval procedures, like purging and bloodletting, which in former times was used against love-sickness and melancholia. Madame de Maintenon was phlebotomized twice a week to keep her from 'blushing at naughty stories told at court.' Conditions are not always in accordance with the progress of science: Injections are given indiscriminately; medications are injected, which could just as well be given orally. Often doctors comply with the masochist

114

wishes of their patients, for whom an injection appears to be a more important procedure, and furthermore the little pain and discomfort is enjoyable. Some of them ask for their 'weekly shot.' Most of the time the injections are not even given by physicians; as in the Middle Ages unqualified attendants are used in hospitals for blood-letting. Dr. Henry Wagner, Jr. in the Medical World News of June 16, 1968 warns us that "Paramedical personnel may become the apothecaries and barber-surgeons of modern times." Some other related professions require a certain amount of aggression or at least dominance and offer a possibility for the sublimation of sadism:

A very skilful masseur used to slap his patients when they did not follow his instructions. Some psychoanalysts have admitted deriving gratification from power in the transference situation. Hypnotists must have forceful personalities, and would not even have taken up that particular specialty unless they derived gratification from exerting power over their subjects. Using such power in the service of patients, they have succeeded in sublimating the sadistic component of aggression. Vice versa experience has shown that those patients, who asked to be hypnotized, have a strong masochistic component in their character structure; often they are outright masochists, enjoying complete helplessness in the power and under the influence of another person, and not having to take the responsibility for their actions.

A participant in group discussions with homosexuals requested repeatedly that he be hypnotized. He wanted to be a child again; that would have released him from the guilt of being homosexual. He did not want to acknowledge the feminine component in his character make-up, but although he tried to be active and behave like other men, he never succeeded. Hypnosis would have given him an opportunity to be completely passive. In sex-play with men he was unable to maintain an erection. His mother had repeatedly beaten him when she discovered him masturbating. After the father's death he had shared the bedroom with her. He could not establish any tender relationship with females; he devalued them. By profession he was a proctologist. Injecting hemorrhoids gave him

115

erotic gratification. He called the anus "divine." He described in detail the painful masochistic manipulations which had even caused him a chronic ulcer.

Tranquillizers, sleeping and weight-reducing pills are sometimes used to gratify masochistic trends: Calmed down and sleepy, these people need not feel guilty for impulses unacceptable to them or to society; they feel a 'better' person. One such patient used to go from one clinic to the other—not in order to be treated—but to request constant sedation, since without it he could not resist the impulse to beat up his wife and children. Many drug addicts have masochistic character traits. They are apt to harm themselves while under the influence of drugs, running across the street in the midst of heavy traffic, jumping to their death from high buildings.

Chiropractors usually count amongst their clientele a few masochists. These patients enjoy being placed in traction habitually.

Examples of self-experimentation among physicians are legion; these may represent masochistic tendencies. For instance Purkinje dosed himself with digitalis; Obermeier inoculated himself with cholera; Lazar and Caroll died of self-induced yellow-fever. Myron Schultz in the New England Medical Journal of June, 1968 describes the case of the medical student, Carrión; He studied the Peruvian disease, veruga peruana, and Oroya Fever. His history shows heroism, tragedy and official bungling. He was acclaimed a hero by some of his colleagues, by others considered a martyr, castigated by his enemies as a 'naive young man, who disgraced the profession.' He had the noblest of intentions, investing in the experiment his intellect as well as his emotions, stating that by inoculating himself he 'wanted to make an important contribution to aching humanity.' One of his colleagues assisted him and, after his death, was even accused of homicide. Carrión went through great agony: he was plagued by chills, abdominal cramps, pains in all joints. He kept a diary, which showed that he understood and described the full meaning of the experiment. He was tormented by a harassing heart murmur, haemolytic anaemia, devastating thirst, and vomiting. His colleagues were so jealous that they delayed blood transfusion even though he was by then delirious, and they let him die. All the daily papers in Lima published reports of this experiment and its fatal result. Colleagues, who hated him, called the experiment a 'horrible act,' but his classmates carried his remains on their shoulders through the streets of Lima.

Sir John Hunter, as described in his persecution of the giant, showed outspoken sadist character traits. But that he was not free from masochism either is evident in his self-inoculation of Syphilis. His selection of a venereal disease emphasizes the erotic component of masochism. He even refused treatment.

Physicians, like all human beings, have bipolar drives—love and hatred—towards their fellow human beings. When these drives are not in harmony, but the sadist component is predominant, they may sublimate it by selecting specialties which require aggression: they derive gratification from power and achievement and try to defy death. Such physicians may become helpers of man. If the masochistic component predominates, they may risk their life in the service of mankind.

SADO-MASOCHISM IN CRIME: individual versus group; sex
            crimes; case histories; youthful murderers; seduction
            of children; identification with dog; epilepsy.

The borderline between an individual courageous act and a
criminal act is sometimes difficult to define. The famous
criminologist, Gabriel Tarde, defined crime as only such actions
which are disapproved of by the social group to which the
offender belongs. Crime, he says, is exercising a wilful right
which one does not have. In former times, as we have seen,
it was not considered a crime to kill one's slaves; nowadays it
would be termed murder. In all times individuals have acted
against the will and custom of their group. Human history—
according to Hebrew and Greek myths—was ushered in by an
act of disobedience: Adam and Eve, living in the Garden of
Eden, were part of nature; they were in harmony with it; yet
they did not transcend it. They were in nature as the foetus
is in its mother's womb. By breaking the ties with earth, man
emerged from a pre-human harmony, and was able to take
the first step into independence and freedom. Their act of disobedience broke the primary bond with nature and made them
individuals. The "original sin"—far from corrupting man, set
him free; man had to leave the Garden of Eden in order to
learn to rely on his own powers.

In modern life the group has gained such importance, that
the individual has lost the capacity to disobey. At this point
in history the capacity to doubt, to criticize, to disobey may be
all that stands between a future of mankind and the end of
civilization (Erich Fromm [68]).

Individual conscience, often overpowered in our time, can
suddenly awaken. The conspiracy against Hitler, in the moment
of the greatest crisis in the war (1944), proves that individual
conscience is able to rebel against evil done by a group:

German generals objected to mass murder, even trying to eliminate their tyrant-leader. Acting according to ethics saves a human being from collective guilt. There is the danger that the individual—part of the mass—has no responsibility; he need not think for himself, as long as he does his part of mechanized work. Once his judgment is weakened, primitive affects can easily be aroused. Uniform standards of living make mass-human-beings do and think and want what all the others do. This is evident in mass spectacles and sports. Freedom and individuality are given up completely, and automatic conformism is the end-result.

The art of cruelty, still practiced in our everyday life as in former times, is changing according to custom and fashion; we can observe that it has become more complicated and refined: whereas in former times a person usually knew who his enemy was, nowadays the enemy is often not an individual, but a group of people: not the boss, but the company; not a ruler as in former times, but a political group. Since material values are so highly esteemed in our present time, any individual who happens to be in a favourable financial position has power and influence. Already by the end of the eighteenth century a book was published under the title "The Art of Tormenting;" the motto was—who does not have a crown, must have a whip. Whereas formerly the indignant people called out 'the end of the world has come, the Antichrist is reigning,' nowadays they are hushed with tranquillizers, alcohol, and television. Some slaves of ancient times led a healthier life than some factory-workers do nowadays: miners are exposed to chemical dusts which cause chronic lung diseases such as silicosis and beryllosis; chronic exposure to factory noises may lead to deafness; workers' eyes are often inadequately protected against damaging rays and chemicals; construction workers are sometimes inadequately protected and sustain injuries worse than those of the slaves, who built the pyramids.

In order to appraise the morals of a group we must consider the fact that in a group all individual inhibition may fall away. Cruel, brutal, and destructive instincts, which lie dormant in every individual as relics of a primitive epoch find gratification. If we were blindly to submit to a group, mediocrity would reign, there would be no place for a genius. Therefore we can not adhere to Tarde's definition of crime. Once the group would be considered the highest authority, all individualism would be abolished.

Again we can learn from mythology: according to psychological explanation myths and fairy tales are projections of motives close to the heart of all human beings. Myths are secular dreams which occupy the imagination of people through generations. Condensation, displacement, and symbolization take place in the development of myths and fairy tales, (Freud [43]). Old legends and tales of ancient times depict experiences which many people had; we find numerous examples of crimes, which are not at all alien to human nature and have been committed in every period of history. Medea dismembered her brother; Odysseus cut off a goatherd's ears and testicles to give them to the dogs; Sinis tore apart wanderers by tying them to trees; Indonia blinded the son of Cleopatra. Such examples show us to what actions cruelty can lead. Lust-murders, committed in our times in concentration camps, seem to prove that these descriptions of crimes in ancient times were not exaggerated, but that human beings are capable of them.

In history many crowned heads have become famous—not on account of their great achievements or good examples, but because of the gruesome deeds they committed. Sueton masterfully described the reign of the Caesars. Tiberius, as already mentioned, surpassed all of them in his lust and cruelty: He made people drink after tying their penis so tightly that they could not urinate. When he was bathing, young tender boys had to swim between his legs and bite him tenderly; he called them his 'little fishes.' Still younger children—sucklings—had to suck his penis. He is always cited as an outstanding example of sadism. Applying modern psychological knowledge we can easily understand how he developed such character traits: His mother, Livia Drusilla, was extremely domineering. Domineering mothers often facilitate the development of homosexual character traits, inspiring fears of the 'cruel female.' Not only did he have an imperious mother, but he had to cope with a stepfather, Augustus, who used him to satisfy his own ambition. When Tiberius eventually had managed to establish heterosexual relationships and had even married, Augustus forced him to divorce his wife and to marry his—Augustus' daughter,—Tiberius' own stepsister, who herself indulged in unusual sex-practices. Some of Tiberius' actions, which may appear incomprehensible at first sight, are understandable when we consider how frustrated he was during his adolescence and early manhood. By tying other men's penis he identified not only with the aggressor, but also with the victim, frustrating others as he had been frustrated. This applies also to Caligula, who had people tortured while he was enjoying his meal. Growing up in military camps, he was conditioned to cruelty already in early childhood. Nero had his lover, a young boy, castrated in order to enjoy him as if he were a woman. Eventually he became seriously ill and suffered for many years from megalomania. Finally he enveloped himself in the skins of wild animals, attacking the sexual parts of both men and women, tied to poles. He had his whole family killed, even small children. Vitellius and Domitian followed in his footsteps; but whereas Vitellius killed mainly for political reasons, Domitian showered favours upon his victims first in order that death might come to them completely unexpectedly. He did not confine his sadism to human beings, but enjoyed killing flies for an hour every day, piercing them with a needle. Justinian was incited to cruel action by his wife, Theodora, daughter of a circus employee. Phokas had Maurikos and his whole family killed. Equally famous for gruesome deeds are Catherine di Medici, Ivan the Terrible, and Elisabeth of Russia. Catherine di Medici, brought up by Jesuits, explained that she just imitated Jesuit padres when she whipped her court ladies across their naked buttocks. Ivan the Terrible showed inclinations for cruelty already in his boyhood: He rode down the streets, enjoying the screams of people, trampled by his horse's hoofs. He liked to torture and kill animals. His actions can be explained by his traumatic childhood experiences: He had lost his mother —his only immediate relative, when he was but eight years old; and henceforth grew up in an atmosphere laden with restriction, danger, and suspicion of the Bojars. Therefore, only in the streets could he find an outlet for his resentment. Later, when he came to power, he had whole cities destroyed. His son, Dimetrius, enjoyed watching the death-convulsions of sheep, chickens and geese. Peter the Great also had an unsettled childhood: Not only did he have to compete with siblings from his father's first marriage, but he had to witness scenes of great cruelty. Upon his half sister's instigation the army invaded the palace and seized his mother's friend and counselor, hacking him to pieces before the horrified eyes of the ten year old Peter. Even his own life was threatened. Shortly after this he developed his first nervous symptoms. Both of his elder half-brothers were mentally deficient and one suffered from frequent epileptic seizures. It is understandable that he had an ambivalent attitude towards them: he admired and imitated them because they were older, on the other hand he despised them because they were both feebleminded. When the older one, Tsar Feodor, died, he felt guilty for having entertained hostile feelings and even death wishes toward him. In imitation of his six year old brother, Ivan, he developed epileptiform symptoms. Having had such threatening experiences with his half-sister, he hated all women and became homosexual and sadistic. He slept with his head pressed against the naked abdomen of his servant. If the servant dared to move Peter pummeled him with his fists. (69) When forced to marry by his mother, he had an epileptic fit during the ensuing wedding celebration. Later he became bisexual, enjoying intimacy by proxy with his friends by taking their wives and mistresses. He delighted in pulling teeth and also essayed to perform a few surgical operations. He even made a postmortem examination on his sister-in-law. Catherine the Great had a domineering mother, who preferred her crippled younger son. Having developed a scoliosis after an attack of pleurisy, she was immobilized for more than three years in a strait jacket-like brace which was adjusted every other day by the town executioner. She is said to have had her husband killed. Karl IV enjoyed riding a horse to death, sticking pigs and wallowing in their blood. Elizabeth Bathory, a Hungarian countess of the sixteenth century, never tired of inventing new cruelties, similar to those committed in the twentieth century in concentration camps: In winter she had her servants stand in ice and snow; she decorated the lips of seamstresses with needles; and used her maid-servants' breasts as pin-cushions, tearing out part of their flesh when angered. She killed over six hundred maidens and bathed in their blood. Of Gilles de Rais it has been reported that he ejaculated upon children's stomachs; they were brought him by his valets, Gilles de Sillé and Ponton. The children were used but a few times and then killed. He also had them tied to a rope and slowly pulled up and down, while they were to hold his penis, until he ejaculated upon their stomach. He is said to have killed about eight hundred children; and he attracted so much hatred that he was burned to death. The Marquis de Sade, who created a veritable system of cruelty, was considered a genius by his contemporaries. His philosophy states that only through destruction is new life constantly being created in Nature and only by crime can man go on living; therefore crime is innate in nature, and man, committing crime, acts according to nature. Louis XV, his patron supported him.

De Sade's novels 'Justine' and 'Juliette' led to a crime, which became a great sensation in Paris towards the end of the nineteenth century: The 'Gil Blas' newspaper of August 14 and 16, 1891 reported the court actions. Michel Bloch, the accused, was a millionaire-diamond dealer. He was sixty years old, married, and had two children, sixteen and eighteen years old. He was accused together with a female matchmaker, Madame Marchand, in whose house the criminal actions had taken place. They were accused by a young girl, Claudine Buron, and other girls, who testified that they had undergone similar treatment. They described that three girls had to undress and were led into a blue room, where the elderly gentleman expected them. He was known to the female customers of the ill-famed house of Madame Marchand as 'l'homme qui pique.' One of the girls had to kneel in graceful positions before a couch on which he lay. He stung needles into her breasts and buttocks. Then he fastened a lace handkerchief upon her breast with three needles, and with a sudden jolt removed it. Only then did he get very excited, whipping the girl and tearing her hair. The two older girls had to dry the perspiration from his forehead and finally to lead the youngest one out of the room. Such scenes were repeated until he was accused by one of his victims. At first he denied it, then he laughed at giving so much attention to these well-paid services of prostitutes. The girls' lawyer pointed out that, although they were employed by Madame Marchand and expected to submit to the customer's wishes, in the case of these girls, their breasts had been permanently disfigured by scars after such treatment. Bloch was sent to prison for six months and in addition he had to pay damages. Madame Marchand was imprisoned for a year.

Since sadomasochistic activities are no rare occurrence, prostitutes are well acquainted with their clients' eccentricities. Usually no permanent harm is caused. A collection of straps and whips sometimes belongs to their permanent armamentarium because a certain category of clients want to whip or be whipped, sexual intercourse being an unimportant accessory or sometimes just the finishing touch. A particular kind of customer pays high fees for being notified of the girls' menstruation and being permitted to suck the blood out of their menstruation pads.

A well known physician had to share his mother's bed during his childhood. He was excited by the peculiar smell, while she was menstruating. Since this experience continued through the age of puberty, he became fixated onto this situation.

Sometimes sadistic activities are not aimed at causing actual pain, but rather humiliation, resulting in activities which would be repulsive to the average person: A male patient could perform intercourse only after the female had licked his anus. He paid special attention not to clean off the remnants of feces, and paid generously for the required services. It is evident that such practices can be traced back to the anal stage of development: A baby is not repelled by the waste products of its body; aversion is developed gradually through training. Normal development can be arrested or distorted by too severe or inconsistent mothering. Since many mothers either because of their immaturity, their own previous traumatic experiences, or their lack of intelligence make such mistakes, fixation in the anal stage of development is more common than one might think.

Patients described a club of anal sadomasochists as follows: Only after careful examination could membership be obtained. If one qualified membership fees were extremely high. Participants were given enemas by a large middle-aged woman, who whipped them severely if they did not evacuate sufficiently. She was clad in rubber garments to protect herself against the feces. She behaved towards her clients like an exaggeratedly severe and inconsistent mother: They were supposed to hold the enema for a prescribed length of time. When they did not perform satisfactorily their bare buttocks were whipped with leather straps, to the accompaniment of abusive language, until they begged for forgiveness. As a special reward for repeated good performance and obedience they were permitted to play with their feces and lick them. After a prescribed period of membership and considerable financial contributions they were offered the feces emitted by the mother-substitute as a special delicacy.

Elderly men, their potency waning, often recur to the use of a godmiché as an adjuvant, although it causes considerable discomfort to the female partner. It consists of a penis and testicles, made of plastic or rubber and fastened by a belt around the waist. Before use warm milk is instilled into the testicles. At the desired moment it is released by pressing a button on the belt. Godmichés are also used by lesbian women. In everyday-life sadomasochism is not always so conspicuous that it is recognized as such; some methods of electric massage can well be considered torture. Some homosexual men do not simply indulge in oral or anal intercourse, but serve themselves of a special kind of jock-straps by which the testicles are exposed to increasing pressure, until orgasm ensues. It makes them feel potent to see their sperm spray high up into the air. Corsets which restrict respiration and a variety of instruments, causing pain, heighten the pleasure of some sadomasochists. Some prostitutes walk the streets in high leather boots, carrying whips, suggesting that such customers as those who want to be treated roughly, are their specialty. Some masochists request special 'massage' of various parts of their body.

Legal restriction would not inhibit such activities, but rather deliver people into the hands of extortioners.

A prominent Chicago businessman, having suffered during his school years at the hands of a severe teacher, walked into such a trap, when advertising that he wanted to perfect his French before going to Europe and was looking for a severe teacher, who would punish him. After only a few lessons the female teacher accused him of having illtreated her and a court action followed. He had compulsively repeated his childhood experiences by trying to annoy the teacher; but when reprimanded, he suddenly felt adult again, becoming annoyed at the teacher, whom, he felt, he had paid, and turned against her, slapping her slightly. Since she knew that her grown-up pupil belonged to society and had to protect his reputation, she took advantage of his vulnerable situation and started a court action, pretending that he had attacked and hurt her so seriously that she had been unable to go to work.

When such individuals are fairly happy and their activities do not conflict with the law, they do not want to change. Those who want to enjoy a harmonious sex life usually come to psychotherapy:

Such was the case of a minister, who was under the compulsion to lure young girls into the church office, under the pretext that he wanted to show them pictures, but then bent them over a table and beat them severely. In several instances the girls told their parents. This led to his dismissal from the pastorate.

The owner of a mattress factory brought his therapist a leash and a dog's collar, beset inside with spikes, asking to be pulled around the room by the leash. After a few discussions he described his family situation. As a little boy he felt very flattered when permitted to attend the parties of his teenage sister. On these occasions he sat on the floor and was served cake and milk; similar treatment was accorded his pet dog, who sat beside him. From this vantage point he was surrounded by the growing young girls' shapely legs, and excited by a strange odour. The dog and he had to sit very still lest he anger the girls and be ordered out of the room. If he made noise or asked for more cake, he was slapped. He became fixated onto this oft-repeated experience. He had identified with the dog and still wanted to be treated like one: being caressed but also punished, at times willfully annoying the girls in order to provoke punishment, other times filled with admiration, but also with resentment. He desired similar treatment still in adulthood: Clad in leotards in order to more resemble a dog and wearing a dog's collar, he wanted to be led around the room on a leash and be gently whipped by a young attractive girl. Suddenly he would leap up at her and perform cunnilingus. Requiring tender young girls, he could not duplicate this childhood situation with prostitutes: He had great difficulty in finding appropriate partners since most young girls were horrified at his request.

When former patients complained, a laboratory technician came to the attention of the hospital director. He had offered to do the necessary tests in his private laboratory at home, at a reduced fee; this was against the hospital regulations. The people, who agreed to the routine blood and urine tests, were surprised to find in his home an elegant laboratory with the most modern instrumentarium. All these patients were elderly women and at first their fantastic tales were not believed. Not only had he stung their veins repeatedly, letting out hissing noises like 'zoom,' but he had also offered them a special massage method which caused them great pain. While they submitted to it, they had to lie down on an unusual contraption in a very uncomfortable position. Some of them had been asked to agree to a special method of being beaten slightly, which was supposed to stimulate their circulation. Those, who had submitted out of curiosity, were surprised. It had not caused them pain, but they were puzzled by his excitement.

He had a collection of straps, some with silver handles, some of different colours, and others with little bells tied to them. After these massage procedures, he supplied them to be distributed among their acquaintances, advertising his services. Since the technician had been on the hospital staff for several years, was amiable and well-liked by his co-workers, and worked satisfactorily, he was questioned only after several complaints of a more serious nature had come in. Thereupon he was sent to psychotherapy.

Having lost both parents at a relatively young age, he had been brought up by an aunt, who used to punish him for trivial offenses: e.g. when she sent him to the grocery store and he came home but a few minutes late, he was strapped. Whereas he cried and resented it when a small boy, he began to enjoy it at the age of puberty. The slight pain was mixed with excitement and he felt increasingly stimulated until he even had erections and ejaculated during such beatings. The pleasurable pulsating sensations in his penis, at first not understood, were closely related to the whipping. The aunt unknowingly systematically conditioned him to becoming a masochist. This explains his preference for elderly patients: they represented the aunt; he reversed the situation; now they were in his power; he being in a position to inflict pain upon them. He preferred those, who had hardened blood vessels, which could be penetrated but with difficulty; he became excited when selecting those, which were located in sensitive parts of the body. The contraption he had built, upon which he placed such females, willing to subject themselves to such harmless games—as he called his activity—put them into a position similar to the one he had been in when his aunt placed him over the armrest of an easy-chair. Some elderly ladies were afraid; others were glad to get so much attention from a man and believed he was seriously interested in them; others became indignant and unwilling to submit to the procedure, and made denunciations.

Among crimes in recent times poisoning takes the first place. Poisonous substances are relatively easy to procure and proof is hard to obtain. The case of 'the missing nephew of Mrs.

Unger' was in the headlines in August 1967. She was a wealthy widow, who, although she was in good health, did not wish to maintain a household and therefore lived in an elegant home for elderly people, the Garden Hospital. Her only relative, a nephew, visited her regularly. She trusted him sufficiently to inform him completely concerning her estate, to which he was the sole heir. One day the nurse noticed a strange substance in her partially filled coffee-cup on her breakfast tray. She alerted the hospital administrator, who had the substance analyzed. It proved to be carbon-tetrachloride. The nephew had disappeared with his aunt's jewelry.

The nurse involved in this case was exceptionally conscientious. Unfortunately not all nurses have high ethical standards. Sometimes they even aid in procuring sleeping pills and other harmful medications. They are not always attracted to this profession by a noble desire to help and serve. Quite a few enjoy the suffering of their fellowmen, even begging to assist at operations. Watching a person's death-struggle gives them the greatest satisfaction.

Pedelsky (70) made an investigation of 'children who kill.' He confirms that undue frustration during the anal stage of development may lead to the formation of sadomasochistic character traits. Murders committed by teenagers often appear irrational. In Bavaria an eighteen year old youth was charged with the slaying of two young girls and a seventy-two-year-old pensioner. In America a seventeen year old boy was arrested recently for the strangulation of a nineteen-year-old girl. In both cases the victims were unknown to their killers, and not only did the youths readily confess their crimes but they admitted the absence of any motive other than the wish to kill somebody. Applying the psychological knowledge we gained from Dostojewski we can safely assume that unfortunate circumstances must have been present in the home and family life of such adolescents, and that they hated some person so violently that they just exploded with aggression, killing the first best substitute, as Dostojewski describes in 'Raskolnikow.' He explains how his hostility originally directed against his father mounted, transporting him into a state of such violent hatred that he felt he would commit a murder; at this moment he had a seizure, which he describes as a great relief, and a state of bliss. Afterwards he felt weak and peaceful because the seizure had protected him against committing a crime. He had not succeeded in barring from consciousness his sadist death wishes. He describes the feeling of bliss in an attack: it is like being born again. Such a mechanism operates in those cases which are not genuine epilepsy. Often seemingly docile and religious people harbour strong feelings of cruelty and the seizure protects them from acting out: rather than committing a crime the person falls down unconscious. Hysterical fits are sometimes brought on by a similar mechanism: the person becomes motionless or rigid in order not to commit a certain action. Whereas in epileptics there is usually a very religious background and they repress murderous impulses, hysterics usually repress sexual drives by their fits. Schultz (71) has derived a method of making the differential diagnosis between hysterical fits and genuine epileptic fits.

If we can produce a fit by appropriate suggestion we can be almost certain that their nature is functional.

A student was admitted to the observation ward after he had suffered repeated seizures in the arms of his dance-partner, a young girl. He was of high intelligence, witty, and entertaining and therefore often invited to parties. He fell down while in the midst of a conversation or while on the dance floor. After the convulsions he felt weak, calm, and drained of emotion. In psychotherapy he became aware of his deepseated hatred for his younger sister. Already in early childhood, he felt, she had been given certain privileges because she was a girl. Forbidden to beat her up, he had thrown a toy-metal train at her, which caused her to have a permanent scar on her forehead. He had taken every opportunity to harm her. When grown up he had tried to suppress his hatred; however he still felt jealous of her, feeling that she, as a woman, had but few responsibilities and could take it easy performing simple household duties, whereas he had to work hard, studying for a profession. Whenever his dance partner reminded him in any way of his sister, he felt like killing the girl. In order to avoid committing a murder he had convulsions.

A young epileptic showed outwardly sweet and docile behaviour and had the characteristic strong religious tendencies. He had been brought up by a very strict grandmother, who condemned sex and restricted his normal development at puberty, forbidding him all extracurricular activities other than religion. Having no outlet, he developed epileptic fits and was therefore thrown out of school. He chose to work in graveyards. In dealing with dead bodies, he found a disguised outlet for his hatred towards his grandmother. She never sought medical treatment for his epilepsy, however, she was so possessive that when she discovered him flirting with the neighbour's young attractive wife, she had him committed to a mental hospital.

A hospital attendant had seizures only when overwhelmed by hatred. He had had rheumatic fever when a young boy and had missed school for a long period of time. When he finally attended school he could not compete with his classmates. When overwhelmed by envy and hatred for them he had a seizure. Consequently, because he 'disturbed the class' he was expelled from school. His very virile, aggressive, competent, successful father, a racecar driver, had been his idol. Now he could no longer emulate him. He completed his education in night school and then learned cooking. He first became a cook and later a hospital attendant. He identified well with the patients because he himself had been sick for a long time and could therefore understand them. When a supervisor annoyed him he felt so hostile that he damaged the supervisor's car by peeling a potato into the exhaust pipes. He felt like throwing himself upon the supervisor and thereupon had an epileptic fit. He himself was convinced that his seizures were not organic. He felt them coming on whenever he was so angry that he could not control himself any longer. He described how he had lived with a young man for two years. When he discovered that his friend had taken his savings and disappeared, he felt so violently angry that he was afraid that he might kill the first person that crossed his path or even attack

131

himself, whereupon he requested to be placed into a strait-jacket.

Out of guilt hatred may be displaced from the other person and directed upon the Self. It can be sublimated through the selection of professions which provide an outlet for aggression, such as dentist, surgeon, policeman, barber, construction worker (demolition), fireman, religious leader (Luther, Calvin, Zwingli).

If an individual is in a position of power his hatred may spill over into murder more readily. Most individuals never commit any asocial action; their hatred is acted out but in phantasy. Originally the attitude towards a member of the family is ambivalent. The component of hatred may be split off and projected onto one or several people in the environment. Once such a sadomasochistic foundation is developed the hatred may be directed upon the Self out of guilt. Guilt is a psychological need—a self protection against crime, or a self punishment to relieve us of fear of greater punishment.

The recently publicized case of Maria Conti in the circus Sarrasani illustrates how a girl acted out her sadomasochistic inclinations: having grown up in a small village in the mountains she had spent her childhood in relative isolation. During her parents' frequent arguments she always identified with her father, a war hero. When she was fourteen she lost her beloved father, had to leave school, and enter the millinery trade. However, such quiet, sedentary work did not provide an outlet for her violent drives. Longing for emotional excitement, she trained in a sport club, doing swimming and gymnastics in every free minute. With the help of an acrobat she was trained for an act on the trapeze, which she finally performed in the circus. She felt jealousy for the more established performers. Apparently her sadism turned against herself because after but a few performances, she fell, breaking both legs. Hospitalized for three months she practiced even there secretly whenever she was unobserved. Soon she was able to perform again even though while on the ground she had to use crutches.

There are a number of professions providing females with an outlet for sadomasochism. Many ballets have become famous for their rigid discipline, which includes whipping with a cane. An outlet is also well provided by such professions such as teacher, governess, beautician, salvation army officer, missionary, masseuse, nurse, hospital or police warden and dental assistant. Menninger pointed out in his chapter about moral masochism how people—weighed down by unconscious guilt feelings—bring themselves into situations where they are made to suffer, to be degraded, ridiculed, or put to shame. Self destruction is sometimes pursued in a subtle way by self negating or self diminishing:

A waiter, seeking therapy, described his life as a chain of unhappy events which, in a way, he had precipitated himself. He had begun to study law, but constantly chose the wrong people, the wrong jobs, ignoring his talents. He had developed a distorted self-image in his childhood: The father had died suddenly of meningitis and the mother remarried. Whereas his father had been an intellectual, his step-father was a very uneducated simple person. During arguments between the parents, the boy always identified with his stepfather. He hated his mother to such an extent that he went so far as to collect match heads and soak them in water in order to obtain the poisonous coating, planning to kill his mother with it. When this concoction was found he accused his older brother of having made it with murderous intent. This led to growing hostility between the two brothers. Whereas the older brother became a physician, the patient—although he studied law—never succeeded in making a career for himself, gradually going downhill, feeling as if he died a continuous partial death. He eventually ended up as a waiter, but even then he was in constant trouble with the union, the restaurant owners, and his fellow-workers, losing his jobs and traveling from place to place.

The dynamics of the urge to kill have not been adequately explored. Pedelski states that in adults it is often jealousy of the possessions or success of others, or acting out feelings of frustration, anger, resentment or revenge. The number of children, who kill, is supposed to be seven hundred per year in America alone. It has been found in all cases that the young murderer had been emotionally deprived. Arson was also found to be a sign of poor inhibitional control of aggression. The victim of the aggression had often been a source of extreme irritation to the child. Other times the child was so full of resentment that he attacked the first person that crossed his path: An eighteen year old boy recently shot two young students. A short time before committing the double murder he had stabbed to death an eighty-three-year-old man, without being able to give any reasons. Apparently the youthful murderers are not aware, who the real object of their hatred is; often it is inadmissible to the person's consciousness, because it may be a close relative—a father, mother or sister. When the young are questioned by police, they usually say something like "I don't know what came over me, I just had to kill." A nineteen year old boy told police that he was bicycling along the countryside when he suddenly noticed a pretty young girl cycling along the same road. After chasing the girl, whom he had never seen before, he threw her to the ground, pulled her behind some shrubbery, and killed her by strangulation, also stabbing her with his pocketknife. When asked what had prompted him to commit such a brutal killing, the youth merely said that he "hated all women." Afterwards a girl had reported him to police for attempting to sexually molest her. Both young boys were popular with boys and girls and described by their classmates as "great guys." Usually the environment is not aware of what goes on in the youngsters' emotional life. In one case the classmates reported that the youth had turned into a "loner" without any obvious reasons. He had stopped associating with his chums and spent most of his spare time reading detective stories.

Bender, who also undertook a study of youthful murderers, drew our attention to the fact that organic brain damage may be associated with an impulse disorder. She also came to the conclusion that epilepsy sometimes covers up latent hostility. Over-restrained children have little opportunity to express hostility; Pedelski gives the example of a boy, whose father spoke to him only during spankings, whereas the mother was concerned only with "what the neighbours thought." Michaelis described eight cases of child murder; he found that bed-wetters had a high degree of irritability, impulsiveness, and a personality permeated by lack of inhibition, indulging in criminal acts.

Lust murders are often committed by persons, who have no possibility to satisfy their sexual drive in normal ways, such as teenagers. Recently it has become fashionable in England for teenagers to give parties in graveyards. The association of death with love—they explain—gives love a special flavour. Overwhelmed by a quantity of hormones, they have not yet adjusted themselves physically and mentally to this new experience. Frequently they can find the needed guidance neither at home nor at school.

Patrick grew up in a stern Catholic environment on an isolated farm. He attended the village school irregularly because he had to walk all the way to the next village. His two brothers were considerably older than he. One of them had been sent to the city to attend an institution of higher learning. The other helped the father on the farm. When about sixteen years of age, he used to hide behind a rock to watch the milkmaid pass by. Once he was overwhelmed by a kind of excitement unknown to him before. It was so overpowering. He jumped forward, throwing himself upon the milkmaid. She fell down, screaming; he became frightened and, attempting to silence her, he lay upon her, pressing his hands upon her throat. Suddenly her eyes rolled up; she stopped struggling. He had had an ejaculation, and upon calming down, he realized that she had stopped breathing—she was dead. In terror he ran home, confiding in his mother, who succeeded in providing him with a passport, made out in her maiden name, and he was shipped off to a distant country. Many years passed; he became a respectable citizen, successful in business and highly esteemed in the community. Having gone to confession, he had been given absolution: the crime could not be made undone; he had not intentionally committed it; yet he felt inhibited in all his activities. He could communicate emotionally only when his inhibitions were lifted, when under the influence of alcohol. He showed signs of masochism, e.g. he was unable to use public transportation, imagining that people sitting opposite him were looking at him, whereupon he would blush. To avoid riding on buses and trains he owned a number of cars, in order to always have a car available in case one or the other might break down. Only when under the influence of alcohol, was he able to relax and to communicate socially. He gave parties during which he went to strange excesses: He made his guests dance upon tomatoes and enjoyed watching them slide around upon the squashed tomatoes. His unsuspecting friends just felt that he had unusual and extravagant ideas, they admired him. All his spontaneous, warm, and tender feelings were blocked; he tried so hard to exert firm control over his emotions, somehow apprehensive that he may again be overwhelmed by them. His guilt-feelings drove him into emotional isolation. He married late in life, but selected a woman with whom normal sexual intercourse was impossible on account of a malformation of her vagina.

Relieved of his guilt in psychotherapy, he convinced himself that the killing had been an unfortunate incident, precipitated by the circumstances under which he grew up, in complete isolation, without any close contact with other children; the family being conservative Catholic, he had not received any kind of information about sex. He had no outlet for his feelings, neither for feelings of tenderness nor sexual excitement, nor even for aggression. Gradually his whole attitude changed: He convinced himself that he did not need such rigid stern self-control any longer. Therefore he did not have to recur to alcohol, which had served to temporarily lift inhibitions and restraint. He had his wife's malformation operatively corrected, and succeeded in gradually establishing a closer relationship with her—physically and also emotionally. Only late in life did he father a child.

The female interviewer was surprised to learn that Filbert was the father of two children, because his attitude was defiant and he had declared in the very beginning that "women should be down below, where they belong, then all men would have work." She had considered him a homosexual. He was of somewhat feminine habits, and one wouldn't have suspected that he had committed a number of crimes, culminating in the brutal murder of his wife. Filbert described that his mother had been overly strict and domineering. She had beaten up his father repeatedly. On one occasion she used a teakettle upon him with such violence that he sustained an injury to his longitudinal sinus which suppurated, eventually leading to his death. Initially Filbert seemed to develop normally and his childhood was apparently relatively uneventful, until when he was eight years old, a little sister was born. His mother neglected him completely all of a sudden. He became almost autistic, sitting on his rocking horse for hours, wetting his pants, unable to speak. When he came out of this regression he became involved in all sorts of trouble, taking part in burglaries and in acts of violence directed against other children. At the age of twelve he was sent to juvenile hall. He became a carpenter, but had to resign from his job when, after repeated arguments with a coworker, he arranged the tablesaw in such a way that the boy's arm was sawed off. He was arrested many times for disturbing the peace while drunk. Although he occasionally indulged in homosexual activities he still longed for a home and a mother, but was unable to establish contact with any female. Therefore he married a twelve year old girl. He called her a child-woman: she could not hurt him as his mother had done; she was not dangerous; and she was completely dependent on him. When under the influence of alcohol, his inhibitions fell away and his latent homosexuality led him into suspecting other men, whom he considered superior to himself, of having relations with his wife. His suspicion repeatedly led him to beat her so severely with his fists that—as he described—half her hair came out and her teeth were broken. Still such a child-like woman was the only kind with whom he could function. His jealousy and suspicion led him to become depressed periodically over what he called "this lousy stinking world where people stab each other in the back." In such a depressed mood he acted accordingly: throwing himself upon his wife while she was asleep beside him and strangling her.

Such exaggerated jealousy is often based upon inferiority feelings. In the foregoing case history they were instilled into the boy by the mother's sudden neglect and withdrawal of tenderness. Contributing factors were that the preferred child was a girl, and that the father—a strong man—died at the hands of a woman. Since his sister was born after his father's death he suspected his mother of having killed his father because her love had turned toward another man.

Such occurrences are not unique to the lower classes, but on the contrary may be observed among the most refined, educated, and intelligent people:

Daily newspapers in spring 1962 told of the case of a middle-aged physician, who fell in love with a considerably younger, beautiful chorus-girl. She had the leading role in a show in a famous nightclub. He married her under the condition that she withdraw completely from show-business. He offered her every comfort. After a while she began to tire of the uneventful, monotonous life of a housewife. In the mornings she sat lifelessly around the swimming pool. Around lunch-time, when men appeared at the pool, she suddenly seemed to wake up. Her jealous girlfriends informed him of this. Her mother understood that after such a glamorous life she felt somewhat lonely and bored, and assisted her in finding a part time job as a model with a well-known fashion firm. When her husband discovered this, he was so plagued by jealousy that he carefully planned how to slowly torture her: He assembled all the necessary equipment. He locked the doors, tied her firmly to her bedstead, and slowly poured acids into her eyes, ears, and gradually all over her body. He did not let the neighbours enter, who had been attracted by her screams, explaining that she was sick. When she lost consciousness, he ceased his efforts.

When her death ensued, a court action followed. When questioned by the court psychiatrist, he described how tormented he had felt, considering other men superior in looks and also more potent, he had suspected his wife of having been unfaithful. He rejoiced in her torments, her helplessness, her crying, and her begging. Only when she was completely in his power, when her life was in his hands, did he feel like a strong man. Still in prison he carries a lock of her hair close to his heart.

Most lust murders are not premeditated, but committed on impulse. The following case demonstrates what a far-reaching influence frustration in childhood can have.

Subsequent to having been afflicted with rickets as a young boy, Helmie's growth was stunted. His older sister was healthy and strong, a good-looking girl, the pride of her parents. The mother appeared somewhat ashamed of Helmie, calling him "my little dwarf," and confining him to his room when they had guests. Whereas his sister did well in school, Helmie just got by. He had special difficulty with mathematics because whenever he tried to concentrate on something abstract he imagined hearing his mother's voice, criticizing him. The parents gratefully accepted his uncle's offer of an apprenticeship. The uncle had a tailorshop across the street and Helmie's parents were only too glad to get rid of him by letting him live there. The boy performed the tasks assigned to him reluctantly, often being rebellious. He felt as if he had been turned out of the home by his parents, whereas his sister, being the "apple of his parents' eye," could remain. One night he was reprimanded by his uncle for coming home very late. Overcome by rage, he seized a dressmaker's form and shoved it against the uncle, who fell down and was considered dead by the boy. In a panic, he ran to his parents' house, supplicating them to give him enough money so that he could flee. Terrified that their son may have exposed them to police investigation, dishonoring their good name and reputation, they provided an abundant amount, indicating that they never wanted to see him again because he had disgraced the family. He traveled abroad, taking on occasional work, and for a long time his parents did not know of his whereabouts. When he eventually communicated

139

with them, they informed him that all his fear had been unfounded: the uncle had only suffered a slight fainting spell, nothing had happened to him, and he was only too eager to forgive the boy. Many years later during a time of inflation Helmie, wanting to help his uncle to save some valuable gold coins, offered to take them across the border, hidden—stuffed in a dressmaker's form. But his ambivalence must have caused him to be negligent: During the customs inspection the bottom of the dressmaker's form fell out and the coins rolled all over the station.

Throughout his life he was filled with resentment and ready to explode at the slightest provocation. Once on the boardwalk in a fashionable bathing resort he overheard the conversation of two passers-by: An elderly gentleman cast a slur upon Helmie's religious group. Seizing the gentleman's walking-stick, he beat him up so severely that police interfered. Throughout his life he displayed extravagant behaviour. Most of his male friends were elderly men; he selected female friends, who were similar in appearance to his sister, much taller than he; he never established any intimate relationship with any of them. He could not go to sleep without holding onto a rolled-up eider-down blanket. In his old age he traveled around the world, visiting all the places he had been to as a young man, when fleeing. He still felt that he did not belong anywhere, was at home nowhere, and willed that his ashes be strewn into the ocean, to be distributed all over the world.

The case of a young man, who killed eight nurses, in a Chicago nurses' residence hall, was reported by the Houston Post of July 15, 1966. Dr. Edward Kelleher, court psychiatrist. and director of the Psychiatric Institute of Chicago called this type of crime a "murder-sex orgy, committed by a sexual psychopath and possibly a schizophrenic." He said eight persons is probably a record for the number of persons killed at one time by a sex sadist. The killer both strangled and stabbed his victims. Kelleher confirms that sex maniacs usually hate all women.

Ronald Paul Martin, on the witness stand in Oct. 69, recited in bizarre detail how he killed Brenda Gregory:

A service station attendant, in his late twenties, he described in the courtroom how he felt aroused by a pair of pretty legs, and this particular woman reminded him of his mother. He felt angry—"something was coming over him"—he hit her, and then noticed a mysterious expression on her face. He choked her and then believed that she smiled. Then he seized a knife and stabbed her repeatedly around the heart. Other customers had never aroused him and testified they had received good service. Only the likeness to his mother and the resentment he harbored against her had driven him to act out his hatred.

A case described in the journal "Stern" (Dec. 69) illustrates the importance of the influence a mother has upon our character formation:

A well to do businessman, in his forties, had struck a prostitute, because her dark hair irritated him. Overcome with remorse, he sent her a large check, but felt so disturbed that he decided to consult a psychiatrist. It is significant that he chose to go to a female doctor. Hypnoanalysis brought out into the open long forgotten occurrences and helped him to understand his attitude towards females, eventually enabling him to marry a girl he loved. Until now he had avoided any intimacy with his fiancée; it was significant to him that she had very dark hair, as his mother had had, whereas the prostitutes with whom he functioned well were always blondes.

During therapy sessions he remembered that when he was put to bed as a small boy, his mother used to lie beside him; but got up every night when she thought he was asleep and went into the living room. Then he heard strange voices of different men. When he questioned his mother, she explained that his father had died before he was born and that since he had no father she had to entertain men in order to have enough money to bring him up. He was never allowed to play with other children lest the neighbors might find out. One evening, attracted by the strange noises, he went through the living room under the pretext of fetching an ice cream from the refrigerator in the kitchen. When he saw a man lying upon his mother on the couch, who, he thought, was strangling her, he let out a scream. The man, disturbed in his love-making, beat him violently.

When the man who had beaten him had run away, the mother appeared to be fast asleep and the boy lay down beside her. He was found in the morning by police called by neighbors, still sleeping beside his mother who had been dead for at least 6 hours. He was adopted by fosterparents. These early traumatic childhood experiences were forgotten, but nevertheless had a lasting influence: he had avoided marriage and was able to function sexually with blonde females only, avoiding any close friendship with women in general. Only when the repressed material was made conscious was he able to cope with it.

These cases demonstrate that the mother is the most important person in the life of the infant. She represents a bridge to the outside world, the first and most important relationship we have. We can safely assume that the man, who killed eight young girls had also never experienced any self-sacrificing love. It took a long time until this principle was considered important in education.

SADO-MASOCHISM IN EDUCATION: Romans; Christians; corporal punishment; love for cripples; domineering mothers; homosexuality; lesbianism; parents and adolescents; foster-parents; step-fathers; education taken over by school, church, state; case histories.

Cruelty has played an important part in education. Morals and ethics were supposed to be whipped into children. Throughout the centuries physical punishment has been used. In many countries children, who did not accomplish their scholastic tasks, were beaten with a stick in front of the whole class. A special rite was practiced in Sparta, where naked boys were whipped once a year upon the altar of Artemis; this flagellation in public was a real festival. The Romans used rods made of eelskins.

Christianity did not advocate milder forms of chastisement. In history we learn how even the sons of rulers were subjected to cruel treatment: Frederick the Great described in detail the treatment he had suffered at the hands of his own father, who finally had Frederick's best friend—Katte—shot before his eyes, in order to 'harden his son's character.' Luther related how he was whipped by his teacher as often as fifteen times in one day. Barbaric punishments were often inflicted because of the sadistic inclinations of teachers. Since cruel individuals are attracted by professions which give them a possibility to act out their cruelty, a considerable number of teachers is attracted by this profession because it gives them power over helpless individuals.

In Germany a special chair, called the dog's kennel, was used in boys' schools; boys had to crawl into it to be chastised. It has been reported by historians that a mother fainted when she saw her little boy being chastised so severely: She had accompanied him to school that particular day because he was afraid, having 'played hookie' the day before; he was tied to a pole and mercilessly beaten. When the mother saw blood flowing from the inflicted wounds, she fainted.

Only in cases where permanent harm was caused did such occurrences attain publicity.

During the Middle Ages even university students were still whipped. To prevent resistance, they had to crawl into contraptions similar to the 'dog's kennel' used in schools. (72)

Still in the seventeenth century nuns were whipped in convents. But even nowadays girls, brought up in convents, e.g. Sacred Heart at Merced, described how brutally they were beaten, sometimes for small misdemeanours: They had to bare their buttocks and were beaten with a ruler in the presence of several nuns. In most instances the linkage with the sex instinct is easily discernible. Women had to submit to male dominance in most countries, but having complete dominance over children, they subjected them to absolute obedience, considering them an available target for their sadism.

"Molly's First Correction" is the title of a well known lithograph by Gravelot; it depicts the lust in the faces of the women present at the castigation. Another painting has become famous because of the subject presented: It depicts a lady whipping a little boy; it is the portrait of Lady Termagant Flaybum, who was known to have caused annoyance in the neighbourhood of Grosvenor Place in London by whipping her stepson every day. England is known for the use of exaggerated whippings in education; the procedure is called "birch discipline;" there is a vast literature on the subject.

London newspapers of June, 1968 brought an article discussing corporal punishment, reminding us that already Dickens campaigned against it in his novels. And yet one century later it is still administered: boys and—to a lesser degree—girls are beaten on their open hands or back for offences such as persistent bullying, disobedience or violence aimed at fellow pupils or teachers. Scotland schools use a three-tailed strap called "tawse." Public schools have a tradition of caning, allowing teachers and even senior boys to hit junior boys. A school was closed recently when parents of four boys complained that they had been caned with excessive force. A courageous teacher had sent pictures of the backs of the caned boys, covered with bruises to the newspapers, which started a heated discussion. It seldom happens that parents support their children against authority. Such an exception was written up in the San Francisco newspapers of June 8, 1965, which brought the picture of a smiling little boy, with the comment: "spanked sixty-five times for being late to choir practice, John Smith, thirteen, received six thousand five hundred dollars settlement in the Los Angeles Superior Court on a twenty thousand dollar suit filed by the boy's father against the head and the former associate director of the Mitchell Boys' Choir."

The well-known story of Abelard and Éloise describes how erotic bonds were formed between teacher and pupil. The case of the German teacher Hayman attracted much publicity in Berlin in 1915. Brought up by a step-mother, he had been made to feel unwanted and valueless. She often impressed upon him that only out of compassion had she taken him into her home. He was often ridiculed by his classmates because he had red hair and was ugly, pale, and short. When grown-up, he was considered strange and 'different' by men because of his effeminate appearance. He dressed elegantly and even used perfume, but women did not accept him either. Investing all his energies in his studies, he became a teacher of French in a girls' high school. Having no outlet for his sex-drive, he became excited by the developing young girls and behaved so strangely that he attracted the attention of their parents and of the school principal. He used to embrace the girls tenderly, tickling them, and squeezing their developing breasts. After impregnating a seventeen year old girl, a scandal developed and he committed suicide.

American newspapers recently brought to our attention the case of a female teacher, who had seduced a teenage boy in her car. They were married with the permission of the parents because the teacher had become pregnant. The marriage turned out to be most frustrating for the teenage boy, who was still developing physically and mentally and by no means ready to be the head of a family. After giving birth to a baby, the wife—entering the change of life—was unable to satisfy the sexual drive of her young husband. The little daughter bragged to her playmates about the unusual tenderness her father showered on her; the gossip of neighbours led to investigation which revealed that the father—constantly frustrated in his sex drive—had led his little daughter to perform oral intercourse with him.

It is by no means a rare occurrence that grown-up people, frustrated, and lonely, exploit children to satisfy their craving for sex or even for tenderness, love, and companionship:

A South European immigrant, shortly after coming to New Zealand, was informed that his wife was suffering from cancer. He was inconsolable when she died a short time later. Not yet being rooted in his new environment, he had nobody to give him consolation except for his chubby eleven-year-old daughter. In tears she promised to replace her mother and to keep house for her daddy. Together in the evenings they reawakened all the sentimental memories of happy family life. Taking her in his arms, he felt overwhelmed with tenderness and it seemed natural that she fell asleep in his arms. Awakening from wet dreams and still having her in his arms, he realized that he had ejaculated against her body. Yet, unable to stand the loneliness and isolation in which he lived, he kept her on the double bed night after night, and the occurrence repeated itself, eventually leading to court investigation, after the little girl had talked to neighbours.

The San Francisco Chronicle of December 12, 1966 reported conditions in the San Luis Obispo Prison hospital, where elderly men are confined. Most of them had come into conflict with the law only late in life, when deprived of love and companionship. A sixty-three year old man is described, whom the neighbourhood children called "grandpa." He had been married, had grandchildren, and had held the same job for many years. After his wife had died, neighbours found him partly disrobed with a little girl. He stated that when his wife had died he felt as though he had lost his manhood, his identity as a man. He had become a child again and considered the little girl his equal.

A middle aged man, coming home from the war, found his

146

wife somewhat cool and indifferent. She had lost interest in life, when their only son was killed in a car accident. They decided to adopt two little girls. He had to work at night and hardly had any contact with his wife. When he came home late, she turned around in their bed, emitting snoring noises, pretending to be asleep. Feeling lonely and desperate, he interfered with the two little girls, which led to a prison sentence.

A teacher, employed at a school for retarded children, came to psychotherapy because he was under the compulsion to indulge in homosexual activities. Punishing his pupils unduly excited him. He described his childhood as very frustrating, since both his parents had to work to maintain the large family; his oldest sister looked after the younger children. Furthermore he shared his bed with a grandmother. His first experiences of tenderness coupled with vague sexual excitement originated when he was cuddling up against her. Her big flabby body gave him a feeling of warmth, softness, and protection. The oldest sister, who looked after him, was of similar body build. At the age of puberty he was seduced into sex play by a fat boy. Grown-up and being a teacher, he endeavoured to be led by ethical principles, desperately fighting the urge to caress fat boys at the institution. In heterosexual activity he was able to perform intercourse only with overweight women of a different race. He became able to function in normal heterosexual relationships only after the taboo imposed on this—originating in the closeness to grandmother and sister—had been lifted in psychoanalysis.

Orphanages and other similar institutions are considered a breeding-ground for perverted sex activities: The inmates are frustrated in their desire for love, and they fall an easy prey to anybody, who offers them some form of the attention and the tenderness they crave. Individuals, who have unusual cravings are often attracted to work in institutions.

San Francisco newspapers of November 24, 1969, report of "shocking abuse" of helpless children in institutions, calling it "an American Tragedy." A Grand Jury investigation took place in Baltimore. In the Maryland Child Study Center ten-year-old brain-damaged children were held by two houseparents and severely beaten by a third one; children were forced to commit perverted sexual acts with their supervisors; children had to observe sexual acts between their adult supervisors. Those teachers who objected were dismissed.

In a boarding school for retarded children a thirty-four-year-old attendant, who had been brought up in an institution himself and was slightly retarded, impregnated a sixteen year old pupil. His father, a salesman, and his mother, working in a department store, had become divorced when he was eighteen months old; subsequently he was placed into a foster home. Made to feel different from the foster parents' own children, he had the feeling that he was not liked, became jealous, and engaged in fights with the foster parents' own children. Once, he recalls, his foster parents punished him by putting his hands into boiling water until he passed out. At the age of six he was taken home by his mother, who did not treat him any better, whipping him frequently and instilling into him that "he would end up behind bars." Thus he was made to feel inferior and became withdrawn. Stating that she did not want "to be bothered with him," she placed him into a boarding school. Not being able to cope well with the scholastic requirements, he worked at various jobs, e.g. in a steel mill, a candy factory, and as a doorman. Since he could not stay at any job for any length of time, he hitch-hiked all over the country. He drank heavily at times, and when he was drunk, he was inclined to become violent. He was repeatedly taken to jail for disturbing the peace. After having impregnated a married woman, he became so depressed that he took an overdose of sleeping pills although he did not really intend to end his life. Identifying well with people in an institution, he became attendant in an institution for retarded children, where he functioned well. Falling in love with a fifteen-year-old girl, who was an inmate there, he married her in Reno and everything seemed to work out well: She was beautiful, gentle, and proudly he stated: "She controls me." All his life he had missed a loving mother. When he had impregnated the married woman, he had hoped for fulfilment of this craving. However to his great bewilderment, he became completely disinterested in her. He had deepseated feelings of inferiority and repeatedly asked in his therapy sessions: "Am I as good as other men?" "Do you think I'm attractive?" "Am I really interesting?" "Do you think anybody could love me?" For the first time in his life he was deliriously happy: He had conquered this sweet, beautiful young girl, married her with the consent of her guardian, and everything went well until she became pregnant. Now he could no longer consider her a sweet young girl—no longer did she represent a desirable sex object, now she was just a woman and soon she would be a mother. However, his own mother had abandoned him, given him away to be brought up by strangers. He concluded—mothers are unreliable; they may forsake you. He dreaded the time when the baby would be born: then, he thought—she might give all her love to the newborn baby and forsake him. His fears might become reality—the cute little girl, his very own possession, might become the much desired but dreaded mother. When he believed to have noticed his wife looking at another man, he was overcome by furious jealousy, he beat her up so severely that both had to be taken to a hospital by policemen.

Sadomasochism may be disguised as compassion and love: some women, who are not very feminine and are unattractive to men, enjoy having power over another human being. They may not show any outwardly domineering attitude, but they fall in love with helpless individuals such as cripples, or blind, lame or ugly children. Not always does that work out as anticipated by them: Cripples often feel disadvantaged by nature, having a deepseated feeling of inferiority. Sometimes they want to revenge themselves for being handicapped. Such children may turn out to be mischievous:

An adopted blind boy felt increasing hatred towards his foster mother. When she went out, he felt betrayed, and when she dressed up, he felt frustrated because he thought she wanted to attract others and did not care for him. Once, when she did not comply with his wishes, he attacked her with a garden hose.

A crippled boy waited at night until his foster mother was asleep. Then he tiptoed around the house, unscrewing all the electric fuses, enjoying the astonishment of his foster mother in the morning when there was neither light, nor warm water, nor heating in the house.

A number of blind men described the great success they had with women. They were considered helpless, sweet, and harmless, dependent like a baby. Their helplessness appealed to the motherly instincts of these women, but not infrequently sadistic women are attracted to such men: The wife of a blind lawyer intentionally scratched him so severely that he bled, when assisting him in his daily morning toilet. How the sadism of domineering women may be gratified by caring for cripples was evident in the case of a middle-aged doctor, who became crippled in a car accident. Heretofore he had but moderate success with females, but now they competed in caring for him. Eventually he became completely dependent on a woman-friend, who delighted in making him stand on his crutches waiting while she slowly called a taxi, unnecessarily prolonging his suffering. An elderly lady described in psychotherapy-sessions how important it was for her to have a man completely depend upon her. She had been married five times, each time to a dying man. Whenever one of them passed away, she sank into a deep depression but soon looked out for the next invalid. She made them do household-repair, even when they were in the terminal stage of cancer, enjoying their suffering. Framed photographs of the deceased men were assembled on the mantlepiece of her fireplace and she proudly displayed them and explained their conditions to her guests. Some such women consider cripples dependent on them like household pets. Crippled children often hate the woman, who governs them, which may lead to sadistic actions on their part.

Mothers, who are frustrated in their marriage, often lonely and emotionally starved widows, sometimes want to keep their children dependent on them, hindering their maturation and thus preventing them from forming normal attachments. Often they are over-attached to their oldest son. This attitude was well termed by Besdine (73) "Jocasta Complex." He describes how such a mother seeks solace and comfort in the love of her child, drawing the young son to her, and then shocked by her own strong feelings for the boy and his response, she pushes him away, creating in him a sense of rejection. Such sons, upon coming of age, shy away from women.

A young homosexual came to psychotherapy. He described how happy he had been in his early childhood, which was spent in a rural environment. But as he developed and wanted to run around, his mother went as far as even tying him up on the sun-porch, whipping him mercilessly, restricting his development and freedom. When grown-up, he hated and feared women, and although attracted by them, was afraid to come under their domination and be made to suffer once he would fall in love with them. Therefore he indulged in intimate relationships with other young men. His mother praised him repeatedly, stating: "I'm so proud of you, that you do not run around with girls, and that you have befriended such nice young men." She must have known—or at least suspected—the nature of these friendships, but she supported them and even aided in procuring them by accompanying the son to bars and assisting him in getting acquainted with other males. She may have been unaware though—of the fact—that he had contracted gonorrhea in his anus repeatedly. Finally he came to hate men and women and, jealous of a male friend, he hid in a cupboard prepared to strangle him with a rope. It is significant that—realizing that he needed psychotherapy, he selected a female analyst. Such Jocasta mothers, says Besdine, do everything possible to prevent their son's marriage, but if a marriage should occur, they disturb it by rivalry with their daughter-in-law.

Timothy was in his late twenties. He showed strange behaviour on the observation ward—physically clinging to and embracing the male doctor, who made the rounds, but showing open hostility to the female nursing personnel. To the female doctor he reacted with suspicion, showing bizarre behaviour, such as opening the drawers of her desk, suspiciously examining their contents, other times kneeling on the floor in front of her. According to the mother, his difficulties arose when he became engaged, but the mother violently objected. His own story was completely different: He described his parents' marriage as having been very unhappy. His father was hard and strict; his mother was unfeminine, she "broke his spirit." The mother had requested the boy to spy upon the father, in order to provide material for the divorce, after which he was forced to live with his mother. Although she was still relatively young she had to wear a brace because of injuries she had sustained in a car accident. He had to assist her to lace it in the morning and to take it off in the evening. On these occasions he saw her undressed and felt a mixture of attraction and repulsion. She considered her son the only joy left to her in life, trying to derive all her gratification from tying him to herself: They traveled around the world together; when visiting night-spots, he had to dance only with her and to his great embarrassment, she behaved as if they were lovers. When he had attached himself closely to a girl, she took him away on a trip and she watched all his activities including his correspondence. In the evenings he had to go out with her, read to her, dance with her, or play chess with her. Complaining about her hard luck during her marriage, she isolated him completely from his peers. When he managed to become engaged in spite of these unfortunate circumstances, the mother had him committed to the observation ward, rationalizing that she feared he might make his will in the girl's favour, and supplicating him not to forsake her. He saw no way out, had become very religious, praying for outside help. She often repeated what a loving mother she had been: she had rejected opportunities for remarriage, sacrificing her whole life to her only son.

Even though these boys declare how they have suffered under the domination of their mother, unconsciously they often choose wives, who dominate them just as their mother had done.

Don's father, having been much older than his mother, had passed away when Don was but a small boy. He described his mother as very tyrannical and in order to escape her overpowering influence, he attached himself to an uncle, but he too passed away when Don was still a young boy. Although consciously he hated women, who were overbearing, subconsciously he always selected women, who were similar to his mother. He was married three times; each marriage ended in divorce after a short time. His third wife was a physician, fifteen years older than he; She treated him like a servant, he even had to do the house-work. One of his wives had been a school teacher. She made him stay home to look after her baby from a previous marriage, while she went to work. He felt as unhappy as he had felt when a child, but submitted to them as he had submitted to his mother, unable to free himself from the 'repetition-compulsion.'

Often those children, who have an over-aggressive parent, may have difficulty in resolving the Oedipus-Electra-situation. The aggressive parent, although feared and even hated, is at the same time admired and sometimes imitated. Fear of domineering women may lead to the choice of an either physically or mentally handicapped love-object. They are considered harmless by such men.

Bruce was very happily married to a woman, who was in a wheel-chair. Her helplessness was a special attraction to him. With her he felt secure; she would never dominate him as his mother had done; she could never be dangerous—she was so sweet and dependent—completely in his power. When she passed away, he was inconsolable, and after a period of mourning he looked desperately for a substitute. He found a lady, who had very weak eyesight, but was otherwise very capable. He rejected her as unsuitable—she was not sufficiently incapacitated. A little later he met a girl, who was on crutches; she held a special attraction for him.

Usually such people are considered to be unerotic and to have little libido, sublimating sex with moralistic tendencies. The emphasis is on tenderness, intercourse being but an ancillary means of gratification. (74) Kosawa discussed with Freud what he termed the 'Ajase Complex' as the main fixation point of neurosis in men, who had had domineering mothers. He explained that the Buddhist king Ajase developed intense feelings of anger and even matricidal feelings directed against his domineering mother, with resulting guilt feelings. Such a conflict is considered to be the beginning of neurosis.

The Jocasta mother need not always be the natural mother of the child, but may be another frustrated person in the environment. Even the seduction of young children may go on right under the eyes of inexperienced naive mothers. One such mother was shocked and surprised when her little boy, climbing into her bed, crawled under the bedclothes, insisting that he wanted to "play doggy." He started to perform cunnilingus and—upon being questioned—stammered that the governess had trained him, saying—"be a good little doggie."

A harmonious home environment is of the greatest importance. Traumatic experiences during the years of development may change the whole character.

A seventeen year old boy, referred by the probation officer, was at first very inhibited during the interview, speaking so slowly and hesitantly that he gave the impression of having a speech impediment. But as he felt that he was being understood and that the interviewer was informed of his background, he overcame his initial reserve, speaking fluently, even using elaborate expressions and becoming very enthused when talking about his main field of interest—space flight. According to the report of the probation officer and the father, he had been a brilliant student, having no difficulties whatsoever until his mother was killed. The boy stated that the family had moved frequently, but he had had no difficulty adjusting to new environments. He easily made friendships with his classmates. But hardly had he established a friendly contact, when they moved again. Since the father was unable to hold a job for any length of time, the parents were divorced. Because of his good relationship to his mother, the boy tried to adjust to the stepfather, always giving in even though the stepfather had a very violent temper. During an argument between the stepfather and the mother the stepfather shot the mother; he silenced the boy by hitting him violently and threatening to kill him too. During the following days the boy was repeatedly admonished not to speak spontaneously but to always think first lest he betray the secret. Upon being constantly threatened and intimidated his character changed completely. He felt as though he were sharing the stepfather's guilt; as though he had committed a crime. His school work deteriorated. His interest in space flight was an expression of the desire to get away from it all. His behaviour was considered slightly eccentric and caused him to be expelled from school. He became unable to mix with his former friends. His hatred towards his stepfather increased; only fear prevented him from revenging his mother by killing the stepfather. The neighbours, having observed the stepfather digging a deep hole in the back-yard and overhearing his threats, reported him to the police, whereupon he was brought to justice. The boy went to live with his father, and his behaviour changed so drastically that he was readmitted to school. His interest in space flight continued and he planned to study engineering.

A growing boy needs somebody whom he admires. In ideal cases this is the father, but it can be a teacher or a hero, somebody, who makes a good model for male identification. Various factors may lead to defective identification.

A minister, father of several children, was disturbed by seeing his two older boys playing war and fighting, imitating the other children in kindergarten. He blamed himself for having brought them up the wrong way. Unintentionally he cultivated masochism in his youngest son by emphasizing mildness, suffering, and submission. He overemphasized suffering like Jesus. Subsequently the boy asked his teachers—was Jesus a woman? He was praised for not fighting and submitting to his older brothers. He developed completely opposite traits to those of his brothers: Not only did he display mild, sweet, withdrawing, passive behaviour; but he also became pale, delicate, thin, and graceful and developed a highpitched voice. Unintentionally, when the parents spoke of him they came to refer to him as she and to call him Joanne instead of John. Under these circumstances it is not surprising that he has become a homosexual.

In the chapter on Medicine the effect of the opposite method of upbringing has been demonstrated in the case of the originally passive little boy, who became not only aggressive but original in consequence of being rewarded by his father for independence and aggression.

In the San Francisco Chronicle of March 17, 1968 Robert de Roos shows in his article that he did not make the right identification and is discontented with his male role in life: He envies women, stating that in his next life he would choose to be a woman. He emphasizes that "women need not excel in anything." In the animal kingdom, he concludes, "the male is a simpering fool." He objects to certain male catfish carrying fertilized eggs in their mouth, but approves of a seaworm—Livoneza convexa, which begins its life as a male, but "quickly recognizing his mistake, changes into a female." In the ensuing detailed description of women's inferiority, he is oblivious of the fact that women bear children.

Dorian's mother died in childbirth. His father employed a housekeeper, and to his knowledge everything was going well. When the boy grew older, the father wondered why the baby was asleep most of the time. Investigation brought to light the fact that the housekeeper, annoyed by the baby's crying and wanting to do as little work as possible, had made an infusion of poppy seeds,(1) adding it to the baby's milk daily. Because of his constant exposure to the constipating effect of the infusion, Dorian developed intestinal diverticula. As he grew older, housekeepers changed frequently. Not having had any motherly care during his early infancy, he could not establish any close relationship with females, distrusting all of them. His relationship to his father was distant. Significantly he selected a profession in which he could feel superior and act out his dislike for women: He worked in a women's prison ward, giving psychological tests to women, who had been accused of having killed their husbands.

To all probability the students, who attacked Indira Gandhi, had a similarly hostile attitude towards women in general: Hardly had she appeared on the election platform in East India, some students in the audience shouted: "Indira go back." Hardly had she finished her speech, when stones rained on the platform, even breaking her nose, loosening a tooth and cutting her lip.

Wangh (75) explains that prolonged absence of the father in the family has such an adverse effect upon the development of male children that the formation of their super-ego is disturbed because they have no proper model for male identification.

---

1. Poppy seeds contain opium.

Furthermore stress upon the father's return after a prolonged absence may be as great as that experienced at the time of his departure.

When Peso's father left there was a time of crisis: suddenly the mother was to be the head of the family. Having just been a good housewife, she was unable to replace the father in the business. As is often the case in such situations, the oldest son, although not grown up, had to assume responsibility. Being just a teenage boy, he felt inexperienced and insecure and was ridiculed by the customers. Upon the father's return, the boy could not find his place in the family—suddenly being in the shadow of the father, and in a way competing with him. Furthermore the father was now even a war-hero: After having been wounded he became depressed because he could not function in everyday civilian life.

During the war the boy had been longing for his absent father, idealizing the soldier—the hero. Now he felt Oedipal guilt for the usurpation of the father's place at the mother's side and for sadistic phantasies about his fate. Outwardly, he showed a passive submissive attitude.

Such boys are ready to submit to a dictatorial leader later in life, ready to become soldiers themselves. Wangh explains that the psychic damage suffered by children and adults in war time may lay the foundation for repetition compulsion: During future periods of stress such individuals may seek release of tension by reenacting the originally traumatic situation. Leaders, driven to recreate war, may thus find similarly motivated followers. Sadomasochism will revolve around revenge, exculpation, and restitution. Wangh believes that the children of World War I followed the Nazi call to a sadistic orgy with special enthusiasm. In modern warfare the whole population will suffer some degree of sadomasochistic regression. Individual conscience is undermined; public opinion and governmental rulings dominate. Survivors of war catastrophes may feel—the rest of the world should suffer as they did. Military service is considered a hall mark of masculinity, the fathers wanting their sons to experience what they themselves experienced. The boys are inclined to fall an easy prey to a leader, following him without questioning. In such situations individual conscience is destroyed; unrestricted destructiveness may follow and global war may render the planet uninhabitable.

Although in adolescence school, club, and state take over many aspects of guidance, during early childhood one identifies best with members of the family. The most frequent disturbance resulting from faulty identification is homosexuality. Although in olden times bisexuality was considered normal, in our present times such individuals encounter prejudice and difficulties. Group discussions in the Mattachine Society—nonprofit organization for homosexuals, usually revolved around the abnormal environment to which they were exposed during childhood. The father was often unable to act like the head of the family, he was disinterested, or not masculine, or inconsistent. The mothers were described as overprotective, or excessively strict, or inhibitive. In some instances the parents were alcoholics or drug addicts; their children could not identify well with them. A considerable number of the participants indulged in sado-masochistic activities.

Dandy, a pharmacist, was very refined. Since both parents were in show business, they couldn't maintain a stable home environment. At the age of six years, Dandy was placed in a boarding school, where he was introduced to homosexual activities by a priest. The boys were beaten for slight misdemeanours. Dandy enjoyed being in the complete power of his teachers and provoked beatings. When the father became director of a film company the family moved to Hollywood and the boy came to live with his parents. The mother, an experienced and educated person, considering homosexuality a temporary phase of development, arranged that he have dancing lessons to give him an opportunity to mix with boys and girls of his own age. Although he became very popular, he never had any intimate contact with females. He changed his homosexual partners frequently. Being a pharmacist, he had easy access to drugs and became a drug addict, taking fourteen miltowns a day mixed with vodka, equanil and nembutal. His favorite love-objects were page-boys. He took the active part in sexual activities with them, but was unable to achieve orgasm, although he protracted intercourse for a long time. Only when he beat the young boys so forcefully that they screamed with pain did orgasm ensue.

People, who are healthy and happy, instinctively do the right thing in rearing their children. Most sick people and criminals come from unhappy families.

Martin's mother was not very attractive. Not having found a husband, she was married off by her family to a much older, rich businessman. He was seldom home and showed interest neither in his wife nor in his growing child. Feeling frustrated, she concentrated all her love on her baby boy, pampering and overprotecting him. Business trips frequently took the father away from home. Not having a model for male identification, Martin developed feminine character traits, rendering him completely helpless, when he came to military service. Unable to identify with men, he made a caricature of a soldier. The mother, unable to go on living without her son, whom she had treated almost like a lover, went to visit him. She procured a large quantity of digitalis by pouring it into another container and taking the broken pieces of the original bottle back to the pharmacist to have the prescription renewed. Thus she was able to administer to Martin several large doses of digitalis, causing him to have heart disturbances. Being, thereupon, discharged from the army, he was able to live at home again. However, his health had suffered so much that he died soon after.

All religions recommend that people should love each other. They do not realize that love starts with self-love. Unless one loves oneself and considers oneself worthy of love one can not love another person. Children will learn to love themselves if parents show them love and make them feel wanted and valuable. Just as a boy needs a good father in his early boyhood in order to make a healthy identification, optimal conditions for a girl's healthy development are given when she has a feminine mother to identify with and spends her early years in the environment of a harmonious family. The novel, Therese et Isabelle, describes how an adolescent girl, attached to her mother, is suddenly placed into a boarding school when the mother remarries. Feeling abandoned and cut off from meaningful social relationship, she is hungry for affection and gradually subjects herself to seduction by an older girl. This leads to masochistic activities. Even when grown up, she is unable to select a male partner. Her development had been arrested at puberty. Such conditions predispose adolescents to depression and may even lead to suicide.

"The Story of 'O'" by Pauline Auréage has been compared to Sade's "Justine;" the question is posed whether a woman wants to be molded completely by men—whether she can realize herself only through masochistic acceptance of her lover's personality.

It is not only important to us how other people see us but also which image we have of ourselves. Some lesbians believe all other girls to be more desirable than they find themselves, which may lead to progressive willful debasement. In many cases they show masochistic character traits.

Jacqueline felt that her brother was always preferred by her parents. He had more freedom, whereas she was expected to behave in a 'ladylike' way. When they were teenagers, she surprised her brother looking at a photograph of her classmate. When he expressed the hopelessness of his infatuation, she teased him, bragging that she would be able to "get" her. She succeeded in attracting the girl's interest; was invited by her, and—as often happens in adolescent games—they kissed playfully. A tender relationship developed between them. From then on she competed with her brother in having intimacy with girls and by the time she had become a medical student she lived together with another girl in a lesbian relationship. They used to stimulate one another, not only by tenderness, but also by painful activities: During an animal experiment in the physiology course, she intentionally cut an artery in her hand, expecting her girlfriend to faint at the sight of the spurting blood. Although all the students screamed, her girlfriend not only did not faint, but did not even scream. The only one upset and horrified at the copious flow of blood, was the professor. Exaggerating the disability caused by her bandaged hand, she hoped her girlfriend would respond with increased tenderness and loving care.

Beryl was born with a scoliosis and kyphosis. This deformity of her spine retarded her growth. At a young age she had already realized that she was not as attractive as the other girls and could in no way compete with them. Her intelligence was far superior to that of her physically normal—but otherwise somewhat below average—brother. Therefore she developed tomboyish behaviour, cut her hair short, and dressed in a masculine fashion. Since she had artistic taste, she helped create flower arrangements in her parents' plant nursery, which was located in a small village. She was ambitious and industrious, getting up before sunrise so that the flowers would not wilt before arriving in the city. She would have liked to be a boy and had contempt for the activities of 'silly' girls. She had trained herself to urinate standing up. As a hobby she assisted the village barber, shaving the neighbourhood farmers.

Glancing through magazines, her attention was caught by an advertisement: A society lady in the city was looking for a companion. The requirements were that she be a good conversationalist, widely traveled, musical, and speak several languages. Beryl answered the advertisement as a joke, writing that she had none of the required attributes but would like to meet the lady. To her great surprise, she received a reply, requesting her to visit the lady in the city. Not being in a position to comply with this request, she wrote back, begging the lady to visit her in the village. Beryl was astonished when one day a very elegantly dressed lady arrived at the nursery in a fancy car. Good contact and mutual understanding developed immediately between the two: The lady unburdened her soul, telling Beryl how lonely she was. Her husband, a movie producer, was seldom home, neglecting her, and was unfaithful to her. She was tired of her hollow, empty society-life and gladly accepted Beryl's invitation to spend some time in the country. Within a short time they developed such a good rapport that the lady decided to move to the country permanently. She renounced all her luxury, giving up the things Beryl considered 'silly,' i.e. she cut her hair short, dressed in a boyish fashion, and no longer used any cosmetics. She divorced her husband, who was glad to be rid of her. When the villagers began to gossip about the strange relationship between the two girls, Beryl's father, by then a seventy year old widower, being grateful that Beryl had found fulfillment, married the lady.

Theo, a twenty year old girl, was referred by the probation officer. She was of boyish appearance, clad in trousers and shirt, wearing a tie and a man's wrist watch. She considered her present difficulties an outcome of a very unhappy childhood: Her father had died of meningitis when she was but two years old. Her mother, unable to provide a living for her and her two brothers, remarried. Her stepfather, an alcoholic, did not treat her well and preferred her brothers. She felt—in order to survive—one had to become tough, the more so since she realized that her mother did not remarry out of love, but because she was helpless and needed a man to support her. Theo despised all females, identifying with boys. Soon she excelled in sports and all physical activities. Her stepfather—refusing to give her even the smallest allowance—made her work in stores after school hours. She witnessed explosive arguments between her stepfather and her mother, during which he treated her with violence, on one occasion almost choking her. Upon leaving school Theo had to contribute financially to support her mother. Being of superior intelligence and wanting to become an engineer, she took evening courses. Female classmates fell in love with her. They reenacted in their games what they had experienced at home. They drew up marriage—and divorce licenses, using gowns from the church choir, they dressed up as ministers, reenacting baptism—christening and marriage ceremonies. These games led to lesbian activities, in which she took the active part.

When wrestling with a boy, the boy's girlfriend—out of jealousy—pointed a knife at Theo, and in the ensuing fight she broke the girl's jaw and nose; since a knife was found in the other girl's hand, it appeared that Theo had been assaulted and just defended herself. She found jail better than home and had lesbian activities there. Upon leaving, she studied electronics and bcame an engineer. In her scarce spare time she joined an ice-skating ballet, where she also excelled and was given male roles. A young girl, one of her ice-skating partners, fell in love with her. Not only did they have sexual activities, but they were sentimentally attached to each other, jealously guarding each other. This developed into a stable lasting relationship.

Primitive man was pan-sexual and so are young children. Only gradually are they adapted to the demands of civilization. All civilizations aim at converting self-love into social behaviour. That is the meaning of the command—'Love thy neighbour as thyself.' But in order to become a loving adult the egocentric child has to experience self-sacrificing love and tenderness. Lolly (76) emphasized how tenderness has almost disappeared from modern family-life. Recommending it as a most important tool in child-rearing, he stated that "nowadays mothers are almost afraid to let a flow of tenderness come to their nursing babies, cutting themselves and their children off from a basic experience of love." The sudden deprivation of love is incomprehensible to a young child, and has a lasting effect upon character-formation.

The mother of a young boy fell ill with cancer. After several operations she came home and deteriorated slowly. She was incapacitated to such an extent that she required private-duty nurses and was unable to take care of the household. Whenever the boy passed the door of her room, she called out to him, wanting him to come to her bedside for a little while. He felt repelled by the odour emanating from her. Inadvertently he once saw her bandages being changed. He caught a glimpse of the black necrotic tissue, where her breasts had been. Having heard of "cancer eating away at her breasts," he imagined that cancer was an animal, and feared that the animal might attack him. When she passed away, he experienced emotional turmoil and utterly confused, ran out into the street naked. Subsequently he was taken to a mental hospital.

Although, later on, he appeared to develop fairly normally, he was always introverted; interested only in music and art, he did not behave like other boys and was afraid of close contact with females, considering them dangerous—"afflicted with contagious diseases." Having gone through separation anxiety, he was even frightened of the transference situation in psycho-

163

therapy, concerning which he had read extensively. Neither logic nor theoretical knowledge could overcome his fear: he felt—once he would attach himself to another human being, he would be made to suffer and finally be forsaken.

A wellknown physician came to psychotherapy because of a feeling of insecurity and discomfort when driving on hills and steep roads. When looking down into the valley he felt giddy and his vision became blurred. He was drenched in perspiration and the steering wheel slid through his moist palms. He was in excellent health and could find no explanation for these occurrences. Psychotherapy brought to light the fact that he had lost his mother, when he was but five years old. He did not understand the meaning of death and was taken to the funeral by his father without being given any other explanation than: "your mother is down there now." When he looked down into the abyss of black earth in her grave, he felt as if he had to jump in, felt giddy, stumbled forward but was held back by his father. His embarrassing symptoms disappeared, when he was made conscious of the connection between this early traumatic experience and the feeling of insecurity reawakened, when driving on heights.

Small children do not realize that the deceased parent is really gone. They realize he is away, but they firmly believe that sooner or later he will return. They do not worry much about the condition of the absent parent but are mainly concerned about their own well-being, asking questions such as: "Who will put me to bed tonight?"

An eight year old boy used to stand in front of an oil painting which represented his mother, who was dead. Believing that she was now an angel and could see everything he did and that she approved or disapproved of his actions, he used to pray in front of the picture. When his father remarried, he felt that the stepmother had no right to take his mother's place. He had temper tantrums and was completely disobedient. When she slapped him, he seized a broom and hit her over the head. Subsequently punished by the father, he sank into apathy, withdrawing his interest from the world around him. All his activities were decreased; he even ceased to grow. His eating and sleeping habits were disturbed, he felt helpless and hopeless. A few years later he ran away from home. He had neither male nor female friends, distrusting men and women. His "angel-mother" had forsaken him, his step-mother was a 'bitch,' his father had sided with her and turned against him. Eventually he married a child-like woman, considerably younger than he and of inferior intelligence. With her he felt safe.

An extremely intelligent girl, a physician's daughter, was discovered stealing from her classmates. She had no use for the things she took, throwing away most of them; she was well-liked by teachers and classmates and could give no reason for her actions. A few months ago her mother had died. Although her father provided for all her material needs, he was busy in his practice and she did not feel close to him; she felt abandoned, and was tormented by growing jealousy of her classmates: When *they* came home from school—she felt—there was somebody to relate to. Somebody whom one could tell everything that had happened during the day, somebody dear, who would understand and advise. But when she came home—although a servant would supply a meal—there was an emptiness, a cold, indifferent atmosphere. Taking valueless objects from her classmates gave her some satisfaction.

Despite the widespread opinion that corporal punishment can not be dispensed with in education, famous paedagogues of all times have objected to it. Neither Plutarch's nor Quintilliano's opposition was heard. Michel de Montaigne strongly objected, warning against the adverse effects. The most impressive revelation was Rousseau's "Confessions." His "Émile" caused an enormous resonance, and seemed to lead to a complete revolution in paedagogic; however, the political explosions of those times, took over the people's interest, so that even nowadays corporal punishment is still used.

Many authors describe how beatings upon parts of the body so close to the sex organs result in the stimulation of nerves, increase in the circulation, hastening early sexual development, increasing masturbation and aberration of the sex-drive. Meng (77) states that the phantasy of the punishing person as well as that of the victim is stimulated. In extreme cases whipping may lead to contusions, atony, and weakening of the muscles, nerve lesions, haemorrhages, irregularity of menstruation, inflammation, suppuration, necrosis, lesions of the pelvis, lesions of the psoas, exarticulation, paralysis of the legs, stasis of urine, impotence, and neuralgias. This may appear exaggerated to a lay person, but in hospitals children are frequently examined, who present such symptoms, which the parents can not explain. Galdston (78) in his article about battered children and abusive parents explains that: "The abusive parent is taking out on his child those attributes of his own character that he can not tolerate, to the point of being unable to recognize them in himself." He relies upon projection as a defense, endowing the child with his own unendurable qualities. Thus, the child becomes the scape-goat for the parents' unconscious sense of self-loathing. Galdston describes the case of a mother, who accused her three year old little daughter of being a "sexpot," and "flirting with all the men;" she forced the child to cross her arms in front of her chest for long periods of time in order to prevent masturbation. Therapy brought out the mother's guilt for having an illegitimate child. In labeling her child promiscuous, she projected her own guilt feelings onto the child, and beat it to alleviate the shame. The article shows illustrations of children covered with multiple bruises, burns from having been placed upon an electric heater, multiple fractures caused by belt buckles, even a foot covered with pinpricks. Most abusive parents had themselves been exposed to severe punishment as children. A considerable number of parents felt relieved when reported to the police: They welcomed the exertion of outside authority in suppressing their sadistic tendencies.

Sometimes it is possible to convince the parents to be treated themselves, and consequent upon their newly won insight they change their attitude towards their children.

In the case of Freddy both parents had to be interviewed separately because the father,—a teacher—considered himself infallible and perfect. Although he realized that there was a problem, he was convinced that it was his son Freddy's problem. The mother was aware of her attitude towards this boy being completely different from the way she treated her other children: Most of the time she was indifferent towards him; other times hostile without any apparent reason, causing her husband to whip him severely. She stated that even strangers noticed that she had changed her tone of voice when addressing him. Consequent upon such treatment, Freddy tore off his finger- and toenails, often going to his room to cry by himself. He wet his bed, which led to further punishment. The mother's inquiry at school brought to light that he behaved quite differently there: He was gifted and mixed well with his classmates. If his problem existed only at home—she thought—it might have been provoked by her cold, hostile, and cruel attitude. In psychotherapy she gained so much insight that she realized how much this boy reminded her of her mother and sister with whom she had been in a very hostile relationship. Her two other boys resembled her husband, but Freddy's looks, character, and behaviour were exactly like those of her sister. Overwhelmed by this insight, she discussed with her husband in what way they could change their attitude towards Freddy.

The number of 'battered' babies has been estimated variously at between ten and eighty thousand per year. (79) It is significant that usually the right hip of a 'battered' child is affected, since blows are directed mainly at the right side when children are laid over the parents' knees.

When her employer died, leaving no heirs other than his infant daughter, the housekeeper arranged matters in such a fashion that she gained possession of his house. She resented having to care for the infant and frequently beat it severely. After one such whipping, she wondered why the little girl no longer cried. Once when the little girl came home from the playground there was a rusty nail sticking in her leg, which the child had not even noticed. Only then was it discovered that she had no sensation whatever in her right lower extremity. When the child began to limp x-rays showed permanent joint deformities in the right hip and leg.

A child brought up with sadism may become a sadist itself: During the doll-play of preschool children, a small girl spanked her doll so hard that it broke. She just repeated what her parents had done to her. Every child wants to be loved; when it can not get attention, it may provoke it by being naughty in order to be punished: At least then it can feel that the parent is strongly interested in it, while punishing it. Children, who do not get attention, may go to extremes to obtain it, even if it means being punished. If we listen to mothers and hear such ambivalent expressions as: "I could eat you up!" we can understand that such children go to extremes, screaming, biting, and attacking other children. Excessive aggression on the parents' part may lead to either active resistance—like stubbornness, or passive apparent submission. Both attitudes are directed against the interference with gratification. Children can not bear their environment to be indifferent. The saying—whom God loves, he punishes—depicts the same reaction: pain becomes lust because the punishment is taken for a sign of love. Overcoming one's own resistance becomes pleasurable, leading to the will to submit—if exaggerated—to masochism. The child is forced into sadomasochism when all his efforts at conforming with the educator's demands are in vain. Hatred is provoked; pain changed into pleasure.

Parents, who are sure of themselves and have self-respect, can dispense with punishment, educating by their good example: Children should not be made to experience guilt and shame for acts that are natural to them but objectionable to the parents. Cain's offerings were rejected; he, who feels guilty, wishes to harm others, because he is rejected. It would be much more fruitful to educate the parents than to offer sex education to the children in school. In play therapy with preschool children a little girl—threatened by the mother to have her hand cut off for masturbating, requested that the therapist cut off her hand in order that she could be an angel and go to heaven. A sadistic nursemaid had held a little boy out of the window. Wanting to do what had been done to him, he held his rocking horse out of the window, threatening to let it go. Acting-out behaviour in children often leads to further punishment and restriction and more severe control, thus reinforcing the child's feelings of helplessness and anger. Such children display hostility towards other children or against animals, sometimes just destroying objects such as furniture.

Religions contain many sadomasochistic features, which may make a deep impression upon a child, e.g. blood-sacrifice, self-beatings, castrations, self-crucifixion, cannibalism, necrophilia, martyrdom, and flagellation; some of which, as we have seen, gave rise to real epidemics. Small children can easily be excited by such presentations in Sunday School. These are often led by lay instructors, who are not skillful in adapting the Bible stories to the understanding of the child. Conceptions of Hell, of God punishing without mercy may impress young children very unfavourably. We are still far from having created a paradise of love and brotherhood of all mankind, even though we do not adhere to cruel customs like blood sacrifice anymore. Often the family introduces the child to sin, whereupon the Church makes it feel guilty. A child's first "sin" is his hatred towards a member of the family. Usually it wants the loved parent all to himself. How frequently incestuous wishes occur in children is shown in curses such as "mother fucker" or the Italian "porca madonna."

That religious plays can impress predisposed children, leading to cruel actions, was drastically shown, when a six year old boy placed his younger brother on the floor, trying to drive nails through his hands, after having seen a Christmas play in Sunday School. It should be a requirement for Sunday School teachers to pass a test in character and fundamental psychological principles.

Only few parents admit that spanking their children gives them gratification. Sometimes they say—it hurts them just as much as it hurts the child—which shows their own masochism. They bring up slaves instead of adults, who can think for themselves.

Stepfathers fall an easy prey to their temper because usually they do not feel much tenderness for their stepchild.

Whereas bad stepmothers have been described not only in myths and fairytales but are even proverbial and can be observed in every-day life, bad stepfathers are seldom mentioned, probably because their activities usually do not evolve around the house, they are busy working and the upbringing of the children is mostly in the hands of the mother. The case of Ronald Fouqué has drawn nationwide attention: he was indicted in January 1970 in Los Angeles County. His wife, Betty, had left her former husband and taken her children with her, to live with Fouqué. Her oldest daughter was left behind to remain with her previous husband after Fouqué threatened to abandon her on the desert. He actually did abandon her other 5 year old little girl on an interstate highway, instructing her to cling to a fence until a policeman came. A neighbor testified that the child had been beaten regularly and made to stand in a corner half of her life. When Betty was expecting a child from Fouqué, his hatred turned against one of her little boys from her previous marriage. He beat him relentlessly with a belt for small errors such as causing a shoe to fall out of a window or knocking over a can of paint. The boy was tied to a doorknob at night so he was unable to lie down to sleep, refused dinner, made to crawl on the floor and told he had no right to live. Eventually Fouqué stepped upon his stomach, placed the dead body into a suitcase and dropped it over an embankment near a desert road. He argued that a father, head of the family, owned the children and had a right to rule over their life and death. Since he did not turn his wrath against any of his own children but only his stepchildren, it can be assumed that they reminded him of his wife's previous husband. Even his cellmates—hard boiled criminals, were so indignant that they beat him up so severely he had to be placed in single confinement.

A young school-teacher, coming from a family of migrant workers, had suffered in his own childhood, and had been made to feel inferior when comparing himself with other children: They had homes and attended the same school for years, whereas he felt he did not belong anywhere, his family going from one place to another. He had been called "white trash." When grown up his greatest ambition was to have financial security and a home. Therefore he married a widow, who was in favourable financial circumstances; she had a little boy from her previous marriage. Soon he felt that his marriage would have been perfect if only there had not been this little boy. Naturally the mother was attached to her child, but the step-father felt that the boy reminded her of her former husband. He became so jealous that he punished him severely for small misdemeanours, once—as he expressed it—he sent him "flying across the room." The child became so frightened that he walked around the house protecting himself with a blanket over his head, sucking his thumb.

A middle-aged couple had a baby when they no longer expected it. Somehow they felt—their peace was disturbed, their quiet daily routine upset, it was as if the whole household was ruled by the baby's schedule. This led to their making exaggerated demands upon the little girl. When still not quite recovered from a simple cold, she wet her bed and was whipped so severely that her sciatic nerve was damaged. Only when she began to limp did the parents take her to a hospital, where they reacted with hostility to the doctor's enquiries.

Foster homes often do not provide enough affective response to curb aggressive tendencies. People may have various reasons for adopting a child: Sometimes a woman, who can not have a child of her own, adopts a baby to satisfy her longing for children, often considering the baby a kind of toy or pet. A young couple—having adopted a baby—complained that "the child was oversexed:" It was rocking itself and touching its genitalia. They wanted to return it. Parents should be completely informed that a baby is not an angelic, asexual creature as religion postulates, but that it is endowed with a variety of instincts, deriving gratification from various stimuli. The San Francisco Examiner of July 10, 1968 described how a mother tried to bleach her adopted child, nineteen months old, with a solution of household bleach. When adopted children grow older, they often do not satisfy the needs and expectations of the foster parents, and sometimes they are passed from one family to another:

Monica was an illegitimate child. One of her earliest memories was of being in a crib, awakened by a strange noise, a man bending over her crib. She remembered that she often cried herself to sleep, feeling heartbroken, during the first few years of her life, when she lived with her mother. She slept in a bed that was always crowded, as if many persons slept in it. She remembers men coming out of the bathroom door towards her bed. The men's penis seemed enormous to her. Once she vomited at the smell and taste of a man's ejaculate. She vaguely remembered that he had tried to enter her. Pain and scolding followed. She spent many nights in terror and resignation. Her mother gave her away for adoption and her foster parents treated her with love and tenderness as long as she was a good-looking sweet little girl. But when she grew into a lanky teenager she was sent to another foster home. The new foster father took a great interest in her. While the foster mother was doing the dishes after dinner, the foster father used to read the newspaper. Monica sat on his knee, and hiding behind the newspaper, he indulged in sex-play with her. When the foster mother found out, Monica was told to pack her bag, and had to leave with a social worker. However, she had felt accepted and loved during her stay with these foster parents and attached herself to them. She was afraid to go to an unknown environment. In vain did she promise to be good, pleading to let her stay on. Eventually she begged a boy, who lived next door, to break her arm. He placed it upon a garden fence and tried hard, but did not succeed. Thereupon she lay down in the snow, hoping to get pneumonia, but she only got a slight cold, and in spite of her crying and begging, she had to leave. She had to stay in an orphanage until a new foster home could be found for her. She felt rejected, unwanted, and angry. Therefore she was envious of other children. In the orphanage she lied, stole other children's toys, and slashed the furniture, out of anger. Nobody wanted to play with her; she felt excluded. When a new foster home was found, all her physical needs were satisfied: she had a bed, new clothes, and regular meals, but she craved for tenderness and love. In the new foster home, there wasn't even a foster father. She sold goldfish out of the pond in order to buy popsicles, to console herself for feeling excluded

172

at school and different from other girls. Wanting to be popular with boys, she indulged in sex games. This could not remain hidden, whereupon she was shunned by her classmates and never invited. She wanted so much to be loved but the boys made fun of her, telling each other that they just "had" her. Nobody took a personal interest in her wellbeing. For years she craved for tenderness and love.

When an adolescent, by chance she read in a journal about multiple sclerosis. "That's it!" she exclaimed and obtained all the literature about it. Gradually she produced all the symptoms, beginning to limp and to complain of weakness in one leg, walking with a cane, and when her real mother heard that she had such a serious disease, she took her back. But being a prostitute, the mother was not able to provide an atmosphere conducive to the healthy development of a young girl. Monica felt that her mother considered her a burden.

Being an attractive youngster, she managed to get a marriage proposition from a man, much older than she, who had two children from a former marriage. Feeling towards him as she had towards her foster father, she gladly accepted the proposition. She wanted security—materially and emotionally. Never having experienced motherly love, she could not possibly give love to these children. She could not stand the children being given any tenderness by her husband, without suspecting him of acting in a similar fashion to her foster father. Afraid that the children might become a danger, a competition, her only escape was becoming ill. Before long her symptoms became worse and by the time she came to psychotherapy, she was in a wheel chair. Of her own volition, she took upon herself all the suffering, incapacitating herself, subjecting herself to tests and a variety of treatments, only to receive love and security. When her stepdaughter developed and grew into a pretty young girl, Monica became so apprehensive, that she subjected herself to a breast-uplifting operation. In the morning, while her husband was at work, she got out of the wheel-chair, doing all the housework. But upon coming home, he found her in the wheel-chair again, clad in scanty negligés, covered with make-up, even wearing artificial eyelashes and a wig.

173

The biochemical tests had not confirmed the diagnosis of multiple sclerosis, therefore psychotherapy was recommended. She had already circulated among various clinics, trying to get attention and never tiring of the search for new love-objects among her doctors and social workers. She was very appealing, coquettish, helpless and feminine. One of those, who fell into her trap, was a social worker, who even lost his job on account of his unprofessional relationship with her. She was furious when she was eventually brought to a female psychotherapist. She described in detail how emotionally deprived she had felt in the foster homes and in the orphanage. She would have done anything to evoke an emotional response from significant grown-up people in her environment, but although they took care of her and were adequately paid for it, she could not elicit from them the great love she longed for. All her passive attempts to get love did not completely satisfy her, wherefore she came to steal, actively lie, and be deceitful. Not only did she maintain several extramarital affairs behind her husband's back but she also began to steal in department stores and had expensive merchandise sent to her, not paying for it and pretending that she had not received it. While a window-decorator arranged brown clothes with green accessories, she approached him, saying that she could combine much more original colours. Pitying the beautiful young lady in the wheel-chair he asked for her ideas. While trying out the colours—brown and pink— she had suggested, he did not notice that she hid some merchandise in her wheel-chair.

Pedelsky(70) in his investigation of child-murderers described that such children often change their position of being passively vulnerable to a position in which they do the destroying, displaying violence or brutality. Monica had at times displayed such behaviour when she was a child: stealing and destroying in the orphanage, trying to seduce boys in her class. During an argument with her husband, she threw a steam-iron at his face.

Parents often describe such children's uncontrollable rage-reactions. Early sexual experiences often include sadomasochistic activities, as illustrated by some of the foregoing cases.

Parents of such children are often antisocial themselves. Since the child's defenses are poorly structured, outbursts of rage and antisocial behaviour are indications of defective character development. At first they kill in phantasy; as explained, they sometimes kill a complete stranger—the first person they encounter. Such an act relieves their unbearable anxiety and usually they show no remorse.

Reginald had been thrown out of various schools because of violent behaviour. His mother, a prostitute, had placed him into a children's home. He always had a sullen expression on his face and avoided looking at people directly. He always had a dirty, untidy appearance. It was difficult to make him talk at all, but when he did only single words came out. His speech was explosive. The other children were so afraid of him that they ran away whenever they caught sight of him. When hindered from venting his anger upon human beings, he tormented defenseless animals: He enclosed a cat in a box, shooting into the box, enjoying the outcries of the wounded animal, driving nails into the box. He cut a lizard into small pieces, taking delight in its wriggling. He set fire to a mouse to see the squeaking animal run around, looking like a fireball. It was thought that if he had a little pet, belonging exclusively to him, he would develop some feelings of tenderness. Therefore he was given a little puppy-dog. But he broke its tail. Later he hit it on the back with a metal toy car, and when the puppy was found dead, he explained that, "the puppy had been so bad."

Siblings who are favoured by parents, are often a target of hatred. When children have to look after their younger siblings, of whom they are jealous, "accidents" could happen. Frequently newspaper reports describe how "the house caught fire," or "the baby was drowned," the gun "suddenly went off," or the child swallowed household poison "by mistake."

Elmer had undergone several corrective operations for cleft palate. Consequently his mouth was slightly disfigured and his speech slurred. His parents were overjoyed when the mother gave birth to a normal child and openly favoured it. They were ashamed of Elmer. His little sister, developing normally, and attracting praise in the neighbourhood, suddenly became pale and began to suffer from a chronic stomach disease. Only when she died was it discovered that Elmer had poured a little hair tonic into her milk every day.

Only in rare cases do such young murderers have organic brain damage. In most cases there is a traumatic family situation: The parents were divorced; or one parent died; or the children's basic needs were frustrated.

Francis was taken to a hospital because he mounted upon boxes in the street, delivering religious speeches, in which he proclaimed that he was the Saviour. He had grown up in an orphanage, and although he had been well able to cope with the scholastic requirements, he had felt emotionally deprived for such a long time that he identified with Jesus, wanting to take upon himself all the suffering of mankind. He had inflicted upon himself wounds with broken glass and razor blades, delighting in the pain and the bleeding.

Since young children are exposed predominantly to maternal influence, sadistic mothers and stepmothers have become proverbial, but cruel fathers seldom come to our attention: The case of a Tijuana doorman, who abused his four year old daughter repeatedly, reached newspaper (80) attention. On one such occasion the mother found the little girl "all bloodied" on the bed. On being questioned, the child said that daddy had "played games that hurt" her: "Daddy wanted to play games, and I didn't like them, but Daddy insisted and I was afraid . . . when it hurt, Daddy always promised me a candy bar or an ice cream."

San Francisco newspapers of Nov. 21, 1969, describe the case of a father who tried to saw off his daughter's neck with a hacksaw.

Sussman(81), Assistant Chief of Paediatrics at the San Francisco Children's Hospital, cites the case of a one year old child, that was interfered with, killed, and buried under the back-steps of the house.

Whereas a woman usually has some motherly feelings, even for children not her own, a stepfather, especially, when he has children of his own, often regards a stepchild as an unpleasant addition to his responsibilities.

Sammy, a son of his mother's previous marriage, was the scapegoat in the family. He had to assist the stepfather after school hours, doing repair work on motor vehicles. He was made to suffer by both parents: His presence reminded the mother of her first unhappy marriage and the stepfather of his wife's past. In the clinic he repeated, "I want my mummy." The stepfather constantly held it against him, that he was not his son. Even at mealtime he was given only half as much meat as the other children received. When he begged for more, he was told, that he did not deserve it because he was not the father's son. His own children realized that Sammy was treated differently. He was not "one of them" and they despised him. The constant frustration weighed him down and—he indulged in daring motor rides, showing that he was capable and had courage. When forbidden even this activity by the stepfather, Sammy subconsciously arranged to have an accident.

The case of Charles Linford attracted much publicity in April, 1963(82): A baby was left in his care, while the mother had to work. He plunged it into boiling water. When police were summoned by neighbours, the baby was found unconscious in the bathroom. Only a few days later, the woman's man-friend beat her little boy so severely that he was covered with bruises.

In the San Francisco Chronicle of October 23, 1967 it was reported how a four year old boy was beaten to death by his stepfather. The boy had failed to account for sixty cents change. He had to stand at attention for six hours and was "beaten to a pulp."

The mothers of such children, being so happy to have found a man again to protect them, try to conceal the murder, not bringing it to the attention of the police. If the children are not yet dead and are brought to a hospital, the mothers pretend the child fell out of the crib or it was in an accident. According to the report of the San Francisco Examiner of August 18, 1967, a lady did not act when her first child died, although she suspected her boyfriend, of having killed it, while she was at a social affair. Only when the second child was fatally beaten

177

under the same circumstances, did she bring it to the attention of the police.

An Alameda metal-smith, (San Francisco Chronicle, 1961) was jailed after slashing a fourteen month old boy with judo chops and scalding him with boiling water. The infant sustained fractures of both arms and a shoulder, and gastric haemorrhage. X-ray examinations at the East Bay Children's Hospital showed that the fractures were two months old. Yet the mother had not done anything about it. Upon being questioned, the mother said that she had not sought any treatment because she was afraid of her boyfriend.

When we read about children running away from home and school out of fear of punishment, and of the frightful increase in suicide in children nowadays, we should question and reform our educational methods. If life has been made so sad, so full of fear and suffering, that it appears not worth living, then the parents are like murderers.

Famous educators have proposed reforms: Guttzeit(83) states that the relationship of teacher and child is destroyed by corporal punishment and hatred stands where love and admiration should reign. The child should look up to the parents and teachers with admiration, wanting to imitate their good example, striving towards perfection. Matthias Giertel seeks to impress upon parents that "material values are of no necessity, it does not matter whether the child gets milk or water, as long as it feels that love and harmony reign in the family. A grown-up person has two ways of consolation when he is sad: thinking either of the past or of the future. A child has no past as yet, and it can not imagine the future, it has but the present. Who would remember those admonitions and act accordingly, could never succumb to the temptation of using physical punishment in education; it is to be considered a remnant of barbaric times. Self-confidence and a sense of honour—says the criminologist Berner, are destroyed by it. Despair and contempt of oneself lead to stubbornness, and the teacher degrades himself. Cruelty is strengthened in the child when it identifies with and imitates the cruel teacher. Sadomasochism may eventually develop as an outstanding character trait in individuals, who have been cruelly treated in their childhood. Although outstanding educators like Montessori and Pestalozzi agree with Berner, recommending methods other than cruelty in the upbringing of children, it is still used in education. Small children hate when their wishes are not fulfilled: when the proper balance of giving and receiving is disturbed, such individuals, when grown-up, may either give excessively—constantly sacrificing themselves in the service of others—thereby harming themselves; or they may fall into the extreme—trying to receive excessively and thereby harming others. The sadomasochist may vacillate between both these attitudes, going from one extreme to the other. If discouraged and made to feel worthless in early childhood, he may still feel unworthy of being accepted and loved when grown-up. Such an attitude may lead to sacrificing himself for an ideal, for a cause, for other people. Tyrants such as Nero would nowadays be considered sociopaths: they loved but themselves, using others for their own gratification. Many sadomasochists are paranoiacs, going from one extreme to the other, easily swinging from love to hatred. Some schizophrenics, masochistically regress to babyhood—willing to renounce, to suffer, as long as they are loved.

A handicapped teenager came to psychotherapy. He had outgrown his braces and without being supplied with new ones, was left to himself. He had talked, walked, and acted in every way like other children his age. But now he regressed to babyhood, willing to renounce, to suffer as long as he could get from the environment the reaction of being loved and cared for.

The baby, whose basic needs are fulfilled, later in life learns to give and to interact with family members, schoolmates, and—as he is growing—with his fellow human beings. When his early needs are not satisfied, he never learns to give and even when he makes an effort to do something for his fellowman, he is never content and happy for any length of time. How sadomasochistic dissociation manifests itself, at first as feeling of inadequacy, depression, and fear, is evident in some cases of manic depression: In the manic phase the super-ego does not function sufficiently, the person does whatever he feels like, without any inhibition, and sadism prevails. In the depressive phase the super-ego is extremely severe and masochism becomes evident. Sadomasochists have often been brought up with severe punishments and abusive language. They identify with the person, who dealt out the punishment, but they represent themselves as well—as the child—the object to be punished.

A good father-figure, which need not be the real father but may be a person to identify with, represents authority such as law, state, order, God. Children, who have no such identification, may become rebels, or anarchists. One of the reasons for the present student revolt spreading over several countries may be that this generation had no proper family life, no father to identify with, since they were in their formative years when most fathers were away at war. Upon their return, they were busy acquiring material values, and in the evenings sat in front of the television set. There was no emotional cohesion in the average family, no exchange of daily experiences, no mutual understanding.

Dr. Robert Furlong, an expert in family relations, who heads a special committee in Sacramento, recommends that young people should be given detailed advice long before marriage. "We have to start at the beginning," he said. "The family is responsible for the development of our society. Children can be taught at home, in church, and at school." The adolescent is concerned mainly with making a choice in life, e.g. vocation, status, love, peer conformity. Adolescent slang depicts active and passive cruelty: "this will slay you," "I nearly died laughing," "drop dead," "I was so frightened I could just die," "this town is dead on Saturday night." Since adolescence is a time of great decision, parents should be instructed how to stand by their children in such critical times of development, when they need assistance and advice in sex-adjustment and choice of work. It has been often pointed out that there is a break-down of communication between the adolescent and his parents. They are aware of being separated by the distance of a generation. Sometimes the parents feel even more uncomfortable than their children: a middle-aged father may feel threatened by his adolescent son. This can be observed in history. Rulers feared that they might be dethroned by their sons and often therefore killed them.

Chronos swallowed his children as soon as they were born. He is a symbol for time. We are all eventually swallowed up—overtaken—by time. The syllable chron—is a common component of many modern words, e.g. synchronous, chronometer, chronological.

Laius ordered a herdsman to kill his son, Oedipus. Tantalus killed his own son. Acrisius had his son, Perseus, enclosed in a wooden chest, which he set afloat on the sea. Hercules slew his own children. Titus Manlius had his son executed. Abdul Hamid had obtained the throne unrightfully and feared that he would be killed. He called out to his son "I wish you would perish." Peter the Great had his son killed.

Just as fathers may feel threatened by their growing son, so may women, nearing the change of life—especially when they have been deprived sexually, go into depression when their daughter reaches sexual maturity. The child offers the parent perpetual youth and immortality; the parent should offer the child courage to face the future, giving an example of stability, responsibility, and reverence for life; the parent represents contiguity in an atmosphere of isolation.

When a plant grows under adverse circumstances, its development is stunted. Likewise a human being will develop unfavourably when growing without emotional support from his environment. Such an adverse influence—even if not exerted by home and church—may later be active in the classroom: A person, who in his formative years, has experienced rejection from a group, can hardly ever trust or believe a group later in life. He may even consider the group an enemy and—becoming antagonistic—may act against the interest of a group later in life. Instead of creating more hatred, punishment and violence, we should spare no effort to make up for having failed the individual in his formative years. It is feasible that instead of juvenile halls, we might have open door institutions with trained personnel; an asocial individual confined to such an institution could be given unconditioned love and understanding. Under such circumstances he would not be punished but

181

re-educated, emotionally as well as socially. Many a gifted human being will blossom out under such treatment either adjusting to average standards, or even surpassing the average and make valuable contributions to the progress and happiness of mankind.

Two extreme forms of cruelty—active and passive—can be observed already at school in the classroom: There are two extreme types: the leader and the victim. The leader will always try to push himself into the foreground, e.g. attempting to speak for the whole class, to outshine his classmates, and attracting the teacher's attention by asking "bright questions." The opposite type—the victim—appears to be well-behaved, modest, obedient, and yielding. He may possess the true humility and intellectual attributes, predestining him to become a real leader in the fields of science: he shows stability and thoroughness. Yet he is made to succumb to the brilliant "fireworks" displayed by the aggressive student. It is up to the teacher to recognize and evaluate his pupil to best serve the interests of the whole group.

Active and passive cruelty can also be detected in the personality of the teacher: He may project his own need for recognition by showing indiscriminate affection or may subject himself to the aggressive kind of student, showing preference for him; such an attitude is detrimental to the whole class and to himself. His counterpart is the young inexperienced teacher: He tries to prove his independence by showing disregard and contempt for the pupils' feelings; this type easily recurs to punishment. The well-trained teacher should be aware of tendencies within himself and able to control them. Some teachers, despite being well versed in the academic part of their work, evoke ridicule, defiance, and opposition. An ideal teacher should be able to assume a role of leadership, inspiring his pupils with respect, trust, and admiration. With enthusiasm the students will follow in his footsteps and become the scientists of tomorrow. Plato and Socrates are the best known examples of inspiring teachers. A good relationship between teacher and student not only creates a pleasant working atmosphere but also contributes to better scholastic achievement and teamwork. Trying to educate a new generation of scientists, we should try to create optimal conditions for both teachers and students, who depend upon each other in their work.

To a child entering school the teacher represents an authority-figure. The child may expect from the class the devotion he received at home, wanting to be the focus of attention. Fellow-students and instructors can help him to gain insight into his demanding attitude; then sadism can no longer go under the guise of leadership. The trend is for the group, later the state—to take over education, and when we grow older the family recedes into the background. Young parents do not realize that the parent-child relationship may reverse itself when they themselves grow old; then mistakes will backfire upon them. Shakespeare depicted in 'King Lear' how the parent-child relationship becomes reversed: A father, who treats his child with sadism—later becoming dependent on it, may be treated likewise.

During the school years we should consider not only scholastic achievement but the formation of character traits: A fearful person is called a coward and despised by everybody. Yet such a person deserves more love, understanding, and support. Fear is part of the life-instinct. It serves to avoid or to overcome dangers. The first manifestation of fear in children is suspicion and shyness. They may feel happy and safe in the circle of family and friends but display suspicion in front of strangers. This is expressed in our language by terms such as homely, familiar, uncanny. We can feel relaxed only in an environment which we understand and master. Fearful expectations can evoke mishap. No one is completely free from fear. If fear of certain objects or situations persists and they are constantly avoided by certain ceremonials, phobia may ensue. Lombroso stated that only the fool, the criminal, and the genius are free from fear.

The smallest animal is able to defend its young with the greatest courage. A so-called "hero" may have longed for death; masochism may have led him to self-destruction. A fearful child is called coward and usually despised by the whole class. But it should be explained that circumstances in early childhood may have contributed to instill fear into him, and his classmates should be led to give him more love and sympathy. It should be explained to them that the most cultured sensitive person, may not display great courage and yet in this category we find the greatest thinkers, poets, artists, and inventors. Courage is over-estimated in our times: The roughest criminal is given sympathy when he has acted with courage.

Besides well-rounded knowledge, education should be aimed at a harmonious development of character, according to the gifts and inclinations of the individual. Spurring on to over-achievement may be harmful not only to the individual but to the whole group as illustrated in the case of Kirby O'Deagan, who received much publicity (Los Angeles Times, January 1965): An overambitious father and an uncle—Catholic priest—drove him on to excel in various tests, which were beyond his capability. Too much was expected of him also by the mother, since he was the oldest boy. Despite scholastic honours and highest grades in mathematics and physics, he was unable to satisfy such high expectations. Unable to get any recognition for his honest efforts, he forged checks, stole a car, and ended up in prison.

Most people and especially children are inclined to shy away from individuals, who are in any way different from the majority. This has been confirmed by the mother of thalidomide babies. Children should be taught early not to tease those, who have some physical or mental impairment: many outstanding, famous people have overcompensated a deficiency, e.g. Demosthenes, and Moses, who both had speech defects and yet became great men. Alfred Adler has given a detailed explanation of this in his work on the compensation of organ defects. A little classmate, who stutters or limps, or has some other kind of disability, may still be able to serve mankind even better than the average person. Louis Braille, who was blind, has offered to all blind people a system which enables them to read, write and study. He lived at the beginning of the nineteenth century; he became blind at the age of three; attended a Paris school for the blind, later becoming a teacher in the same school. He wrote a manual of arithmetic for the blind, invented the alphabet consisting of dots, and was instrumental in establishing schools for the blind, which then spread rapidly all over Europe. Some people refuse to let the "handicap handicap them" and even become famous, e.g. Saundersen, an English blind mathematician, became professor of mathematics and physics at Cambridge University; Thomas Blacklock became doctor of theology in Edinburgh. A contemporary New York attorney—upon becoming blind, refused to learn Braille, and considered it masochism to be in the company of blind people.

Most of those who are born blind hold their mother responsible. Even in a case where the father had caused the mother to have an intrauterine infection, the mother was blamed by the blind son, who stated—she created me like that.

Ellsworth came to our attention because of the development of masochist character traits, which were in a way connected with his blindness: He too blamed his mother for his disability, emphasizing that she had married a cousin. He still remembers how miserable he felt when he was sent to a London school for the blind, whereas his healthy brother remained at home in another city.

His case confirms the oft repeated experience, that children placed in institutions at an early age, feel rejected, especially when they have healthy siblings. He felt expelled, amongst strange people, cried, and walked around by himself. Special attention was given at the school to those, who displayed any particular talent, e.g. one of his classmates was given private music lessons and later became a famous composer. However, Ellsworth had no special gift for anything. Trying to prove to himself that he was equal to others, he did not succeed. Not even in swimming and dancing classes was he able to do as well as his classmates. He was the only one, who did not learn to dance. He was pushed around by the other boys and ended up being a wallflower, feeling lonely. In his despair he sneaked into the girls' dormitory of the school and befriended a girl, indulging in sex activities at the age of only sixteen. The girl, being the only daughter of a wealthy businessman, was permitted to go home on weekends. On these occasions, she invited him to come along and introduced him to her father;

gradually having become attached to each other, they became engaged. The girl's father whole-heartedly accepted him as his son-in-law and it was decided that they should get married upon graduation. The father emphasized that there would be no necessity for the boy to make a living, since he would provide amply for the young couple. He was happy that his daughter had found a bridegroom despite his serious handicap and welcomed Ellsworth with open arms. Finally Ellsworth had found acceptance and compensation for his memories of early traumatic experiences: e.g. His mother, blamed by family and church for having married a cousin, felt guilty and inferior to mothers, who had normal children. When she took him to the park, she avoided other mothers in order to escape their pitying remarks. When they did meet other women there were always so many "buts," e.g. ". . . but he has blond hair;" " . . . he is tall for his age;" " . . . but he seems so intelligent." All his attempts to play with other children went wrong: He bumped into them and couldn't see their toys. Being ashamed of him, his healthy brother took him along only when he was forced to and when they met other children he said: "Turn your head away so they won't see your eyes." At times, the mother unable to stand the strain, went home to her own family. During such periods the father took to drinking, nobody looked after the boys, there was no food in the house, and the boys fed on chocolate bars.

Having a handicapped child is usually a terrible strain on the relatives, who feel relieved when the child is sent to a boarding school. This helps us to understand the bliss Ellsworth felt, when he had finally found what he wanted all his life. All his new-found happiness came to a sudden end during the London Blitz: One weekend, while Ellsworth had stayed behind at school, father and daughter were killed by a bomb. Ellsworth changed his whole personality, falling back upon an earlier stage of development. For some time he sat around brooding, with his head in his hands, refusing any kind of activity. He fell into a deep depression, even refusing food. Antidepressants aroused him from his passivity, however, he resisted regular work and began to steal, accumu-

186

lating stacks of objects, completely useless to him such as linen, cutlery, kitchenware, which represented to him a substitute for the household he had almost attained. Although—by his dramatic experiences, he appeared to be more desirable to other girls now, he refused to have any contact with them. He hated all women. Years later he managed to get married. He succeeded to have sexual intercourse; but at the height of orgasm, he used to bite his wife so viciously that her face, neck, and shoulders were covered with scars. Unable to stand it any longer, she abandoned him, going to another country.

OUTLOOK: significance for world government.

The deepest problems of modern life derive from the claim of the individual to preserve the autonomy and individuality of his existence in the face of overwhelming social forces: If he stands against the group, he may be forced to be a martyr—be it for science, religion, race, war, or whatever ideal the group has chosen to live by. Although obedience to authority seems basic to the very survival of society, it may also be among the most potentially destructive of psychological mechanisms. We recall how many guards and attendants of the death camps and gas chambers of Nazi Germany defended themselves during the trial with the statement: "I did nothing wrong, I simply obeyed orders." From early infancy we are trained to be conformists. Only a few people listen to their conscience and act accordingly, having the courage not to conform under certain circumstances: e.g. The psychiatrist, Dr. Karl Henry Koster, in Copenhagen, earned world fame by not conforming: he led hundreds of Jews to Bispebjerg Hospital, creating a clandestine shelter for almost two thousand people, in the psychiatry building. This was the first step in the underground operation that smuggled them to neutral Sweden, where they were free from the threat of deportation to Germany's extermination camps. Money was collected for them, amounting to more than two hundred thousand dollars. Such actions demonstrate that man is able to act according to reason and ethical principles. If an individual were to adjust to the norm of his group under any circumstances, a Jew maintaining his faith during the Nazi Regime, would be considered abnormal; Jesus would have been considered a masochist, and Francis of Assisi a schizophrenic. A compromise has to be found between being a conformist and an individualist. We have to build a brotherhood by conforming and yet—at times—we have to rebel, searching for new directions, effecting change, creating new dimensions.

Education should be aimed at developing conscience, sympathy for fellow-human beings, and moral conduct. Instruction in history in school consists mainly in an enumeration of war and crime. Children do not learn that war destroys human life and soil, culture, and industry. Cruelty in war has increased so that, where formerly a certain number of soldiers were killed, nowadays whole countries face annihilation. An individual murderer kills just one person; cruel rulers killed whole nations for their ambition. The individual knows very little about his governors. The San Francisco Chronicle of July 18, 1967 reported how on election day a deodorant manufacturer advertised a foot powder by distributing leaflets, using the slogan "For Mayor—Honourable Pulvapies." The coastal town Picoaza selected "Pulvapies" by a clear majority and a great number of other cities had marked their ballots for it. This shows that highly qualified leaders are needed in order that culture and refinement do not sink to the level of the uneducated majority.

Modern governments use propaganda, semantics, and indoctrination. At a medical convention it was proposed that Tri-cyano-amino-propene be added to drinking water to render the population and the army more easily amenable to suggestion by the government. The question was raised whether neurosurgery, drug-therapy, and hypnosis would be in the service of a political elite to enslave the minds of the people.

The Medical World of May, 1967 warned of the danger of self-destruction, admonishing us to take a look at the forces shaping the contemporary world, enumerating "wholesale murder, continuous war, increased use of radioactive substances without provision for protection, abortion by compulsion." Since the discovery of methods of nuclear fission and the perfection of techniques for biological and chemical aggression humanity—for the first time—has acquired the power for universal self-destruction.

A past president of the New York Academy of Sciences in January 1967 proposed as a solution the formation of a small group, representing the scientific and technological minority, to guide governments in their contribution to the welfare of mankind. Every age requires a new concept of government, which would bring new visions of good life for humanity. Only such a trained segment of mankind can influence decisions affecting the welfare of all humanity. If we had such a group, maybe war would not be a necessity, but a remnant from barbaric times—a children's disease of mankind.

Freud explained in "Civilization and its Discontents" that modern man finds little gratification in our kind of civilization, but that our inborn drives can be sublimated—expressed in more refined ways.

THE MODERN OEDIPUS: case history.

The following case which we may call "A modern Oedipus" demonstrates that topics presented in myths and fairy tales as mentioned heretofore are not alien to modern man. Under special circumstances people may be overpowered by their drives.

Wilfred, a middle-aged gentleman, was of distinguished appearance: tall, slender, unobtrusively elegant—but he was blind. He gave his history, carefully choosing his expressions, and displayed a small scar in his right temple.

His father, a farmer, lost his wife when his children were teenagers. Needing someone to take care of the house and children, he married an unattractive old maid from a nearby village, who welcomed this late chance to get married. Not only did she have to look after the household, but she also had to help with the farm-work. Therefore their newly born baby, Wilfred, was left under the care of his oldest step-sister. He remembered that she attended school when he was a small boy, that he was left alone most of the time, often crying with hunger and discomfort, fed at irregular intervals, feeling cold and wet. Since his stepsister and brothers were much older, he had no playmates. He attended elementary school in a nearby village, whenever his father could drive him there. The father had a violent temper. Wilfred often overheard his parents quarreling violently, and being afraid of his father, identified with his mother.

After one such quarrel the mother packed a bag and left without giving any explanation. For such a little boy that was incomprehensible: Where did she go? Would she come back? When? What would happen in the meantime? These questions revolved in his head; he was frightened. After a few weeks, the father brought her back, explaining that she had gone to stay with her family.

In his spare time Wilfred helped his father on the farm, since the older brothers had been sent to the city to attend school. Once, when driving cattle to be slaughtered, a calf strayed, whereupon his father—overcome with rage—beat him with a bull's pizzle till he sank to the turf, unconscious.

When he had reached high school age, he was sent to the city too. He lived together with his oldest step-brother, with whom he was on very good terms; he represented the good father, for whom Wilfred had always longed. Wilfred was of very good intelligence, could easily cope with the scholastic requirements, mixed well with his classmates, although he was somewhat shy and not interested in girls. After having received a college education, he entered the step-brother's business in the city. By then the father had passed away; the stepsister was married; the mother still lived in the village.

He felt completely at home in the step-brother's house: The step-brother and his wife gave him all the love and attention he had missed in his childhood. They were like parents. Only now did he have a real home. He blossomed out: Under the guidance of his step-brother he became "a man of the world," was introduced into society, and traveled extensively.

His sister-in-law was like a mother to him; he could confide in her. He admired and respected her. Gradually, imperceptibly, a flow of tenderness crept into their relationship. Since he had never experienced such closeness, they all considered it natural. The sister-in-law treated him like a boy, tending to each of his whims. It came as a surprise to him, when he noticed that he had not only tender feelings, but was also sexually attracted to her. To their dismay their mutual attraction developed into a passion.

The sister-in-law—unsure of herself and guiltridden, vacillated between attracting him and repelling him.

Wilfred was caught in a serious conflict with his conscience: His brother had done so much for him; everything he had, everything he was, he owed to him. He decided to transfer to another city, but the brother was dismayed and did not want to part with him. Eventually they openly discussed the matter together. The brother did not make a scene as Wilfred had feared. He stated that he loved them both; considering Wilfred's unhappy childhood, he could understand how Wilfred came to feel like this. He loved him dearly like a son; he did not think this relationship would last. He decided to go on a trip around the world, staying in each place as long as he liked it, and would just wait and see what would become of this relationship, which he called "Wilfred's childhood disease."

Weighed down by guilt and doubts, the couple was not as happy as expected. Many times they decided to discontinue their relationship but were unable to keep up their resolution.

The brother wrote regularly, asking them to inform him when they wanted him to return. He informed them regularly of his whereabouts and appeared to have an interesting trip, describing the various places he visited. For a while they did not hear from him; then they were notified that he had committed suicide.

Initially they were guilt-stricken, but after they had overcome this period of deep mourning, the sister-in-law indicated that, nothing standing between them anymore, they should get married. But he felt depressed, guilty, unable to perform as he had done before; his passion had cooled off; he moved to different living quarters; he could not possibly leave altogether, because not only did he have to take care of the business, but she being an inexperienced housewife, needed his advice and assistance in all necessary formalities. Whereas she did not appear to feel or act differently, Wilfred's depression intensified. He could not go on living like that any longer. He decided to follow his brother—to commit suicide. He bought a pistol, but—being frightened, he placed it under his pillow and decided to wait until morning, unconsciously expecting that it would go off "accidentally" during the night. Consciously he wanted to postpone the decision, believing that after a good night's sleep he might feel differently. He hardly slept all night. At dawn he felt, he should not possibly wait any longer, he should finally "do it" and have it over with. He had never had a pistol in his hands before but had read in novels that one is supposed to press it against one's temple. Standing in front of the mirror, he pressed it against his temple, as described in the novels, and pulled the trigger.

His cleaning woman, coming early in the morning, found him lying on the floor in a pool of blood, and took him to the hospital in an ambulance. He was not dead, but found to be in a critical condition. Having shot himself through the optic nerves, he could never see again, even though he recovered.

When doctors suggested an electronic device to enable him to be somewhat more independent, he refused it, saying "I want to remain blind; I do not want to see." By the time he came to psychotherapy he had married his sister-in-law. Now he was helpless and she had to take care of him. He instructed her how to conduct their business; they lived in comfortable circumstances, he stated that he was as content as could be expected under the circumstances, however his unconscious guilt found expression in various somatic complaints: headache, numbness, and sleeplessness. He tormented his wife with jealousy; he accompanied her everywhere, even to the dressmaker and to the hairdresser. Whenever they traveled he attracted attention everywhere they went, because he was still very good-looking and entertaining. He made an effort to arouse the interest of women, but took delight in being rude as soon as they responded. The couple had a circle of superficial acquaintances. He used his man-friends to serve his own interests, such as helping him in his business, or driving him in their car. He went from one doctor to the other, telling his history in detail, but not following any advice, and leaving before therapy could even be started. Whenever he believed that his wife was not affectionate enough, he advertised for a "submissive secretary" or for an "attractive housekeeper," and there was constant turmoil in his life.

In his masochistic attitude Wilfred subconsciously arranged to blind himself so that he would be punished and be a martyr. He didn't really love anybody. He needed his wife, but he used her as he used his man-friends, to serve his own interests.

BIBLIOGRAPHY

1. Montesquieu: "De l'Esprit des Lois" Génève (1748)
2. Nietzsche: "Zarathustra"
3. Andreas-Salomé: "Friedrich Nietzsche in seinen Werken" Wien (1894)
4. Eisler: "Perverted Psychiatry" Amer. J. Psychiat. 23:11 (May, 1967)
5. Hoppe: "Persecution and Conscience" Am. J. Psychother. 52(1):106 (1965)
6. Bak, Robert "Masochism in Paranoia" Psychoan. Quart. 15(3):285 (1964)
7. Krafft-Ebing "Psychopathia Sexualis" Stuttgart (1903)
8. Plunket-Woodgate "Things Seen at the Tower of London" Seeley Service & Co. London (1928)
9. Benham "The Tower of London" London (1906)
10. Achelis, Thomas "Ecstasy in Religion and Art" Berlin (1902)
11. Shaftesbury,—Cooper, Anthony A. "Characteristics of Men" London
12. Charcot "Leçon sur la Maladie du Système Nerveux fait a la Salpétriere" Archives Salpétriere
13. Bain, Alexander "Mental & Moral Science"
14. The Sciences 6(9):11 (Feb. 1967) "Dances of Courtship"
15. Malebranche, Nicolas de "Recherche de la Vérité"
16. Lavater, Johann Kaspar "Physiognomie" 3:157 London (1804)
17. Rousseau "Émile" "Confessions"
18. Perls, Frederick "Ego Hunger & Aggression" Orbit Graphic Arts, San Francisco
19. Sade, Marquis de "Romans" "Les Crimes de l'Amour" Bruxelles 1881 "Justine, ou les Malheurs de la Vertu" Paris 1889

20. Sacher—Masoch: "Die Liebe" Stuttgart (1870); "Memoiren" Berlin (1906); "Das Eigentum" Bern (1877)
21. Dostojewski: "Collected Works"
22. Schnitzler, Arthur: "Gesammelte Werke" Fischer Verlag (1921)
23. Wedekind, Frank: "Collected Works" Nieten
24. Havelock-Ellis: "Collected Works"
25. Eulenburg, Albert: "Sadismus und Masochismus" Wiesbaden (1902)
26. Shakespeare. "Collected Works" Mitchell-Kennerley (1923)
27. Goethe: "Collected Works" Max Hesse Verlag, Leipzig
28. Kleist: "Penthesilea"
29. Poe, Edgar Allan: "The Tell-Tale Heart"
30. Hawthorne, Nathaniel: "Rappaccini's Daughter"
31. Dostojewski: "Raskolnikow" "Crime and Punishment"
32. Boccaccio: "Decamerone" Bologna (1875)
33. D'Annunzio: "Il Piacere"
34. Zola: "Collected Works" "L'Assommoir" Grand Carteret: "Zola en Image" Paris (1906)
35. Sudermann: "Salomé"
36. Wilde, Oscar: "Salomé"
37. Hugo, Victor: "Notre Dame de Paris" Dupuys: "Victor Hugo—l'Homme et le Poet" Paris 1902
38. Flaubert: "Salambo" E. Faguet: "Flaubert" Paris (1899)
39. Maupassant, Guy de: "Fort comme la Mort" "Collected Works" Ompteda, Paris (1903)
40. Grimm: "Fairy Tales"
41. Wertham, Frederick: "Dark Legend"
42. Groddeck, Georg: "Das Buch vom Es" Internat. Psychoan. Verl. Leipzig, Wien, Zürich 1926
43. Freud: "Collected Papers"
44. Stekel: "Disorders of the Instinct and Emotions" "Interpretation of Dreams" Livewright Publ. Corp. N.Y.
45. Fenichel, Otto: "The Psychoanalytic Theory of Neurosis" Norton, New York (1945)
46. Menninger: "Man Against Himself" "The Human Mind" Harcourt, Brace & Co. New York
47. Spitz, René: "Anaclitic Depression"

48. Fromm-Reichmann, Frieda: "Schizophrenia"
49. Kretschmer: "Physique and Character" Rutledge (1950)
50. Sheldon, William: "Constitutional Psychology"
51. Koster: "Handwriting in Mental Disease" Johann Ambrosius Barth, Leipzig (1903)
52. Wieser, Roda: "Die Handschrift der Verbrecher" Verl. Julius Springer (1933)
53. Becker, M.: "Graphologie der Kinderschrift" Niels Kampmann Verl. (1930) Heidelberg
54. Kanfer, Alfred: Strang Clinic, New York "Early Detection of Cancer in Handwriting"
55. "Kamasutra" Hermann Barsdorf Verl. (1922)
56. Bram, Joseph: "Change and Choice in Ethnic Identification" New York Academy of Sciences, (December 1965)
57. Schoeps, Hans Joachim: "Unbewältigte Geschichte" Harder & Spenersche, Berlin (1964)
58. Waitz, Theodore: "Anthropologie" Stuttgart
59. Wuttke, Adolph: "Handbuch der Christlichen Sittenlehre" Stuttgart
60. Braid: "Observation on Trance by Human Hibernation" London (1850)
61. Reik, Theodor: "Listening with the Third Ear"
62. Haxthausen, August: "Constitution of Russia" Petersburg
63. Steffens, Henrik: "False Theories and True Belief"
64. Pelinkan & Raskolniken: "Legal-Medical Investigations of Skoptsis" Plutarch, Petersburg
65. Hammer, Wilhelm: Monthly J. Dis. Ur. Tract 1.hg.H III
66. Stern: "History of Public Customs in Russia" I:384, II:49-50
67. Plaettner: "Eros in Prison"
68. Fromm, Eric:
69. Dale: "Medical Biographies" Univ. Okla. Press (1952)
70. Pedelsky, Edward: "Children Who Kill" Amer. Family Physician 9(2) (August, 1965)
71. Schulz: "Autogenic Training"
72. Schmidt: "History of Paedagogic" Vol. III:171
73. Besdine: "Jocasta and Oedipus" Pathways (March, 1968)

197

74. Okonongi, K.: "Some Comments on Psychoanalysis in Japan" Psychosomatic Soc. 7:297 (1967)
75. Wangh: "Frontiers of Clinical Psychiatry" 4.15.68
76. Lolli: Convention California Spring (1965)
77. Meng: "Strafen und Erziehen"
78. Gladston: Medical Image (August 1968)
79. N.E.J.M. 279(1):48
80. Confidential Flash (April, 1967)
81. Sussman, Sidney: S. F. Gen. Hosp. (July 1966) S. F. Examiner
82. Yamamoto, Joe: "The Tattooed Man" J. Nerv. Ment. Dis. 136(4) (April, 1963)
83. World Medical Journal 12(2) (1965)
84. Spranger, Eduard: "Psychologie des Jugendalters" Quelle & Meyer, Leipzig (1925)
85. Pestalozzi, Heinrich: "Schriften" Velhagen & Klasing, Leipzig (1921)
86. Bernfeld, Siegfried: "Sisyphos—Limits of Education" Internat. Psychoanal. Verlag, Wien
87. Handbook of American Institutions
88. Handbook of Classification in Correctional Institutions
89. Heinemann, William: "The Montessori Method Applied to Child Education" London
90. Perkins, John Forbes: "Common Sense and Bad Boys"
91. Ross, James S.: "Groundwork of Educational Psychology" Harrap, London (1936)
92. Reik, Theodor: "The Unknown Murderer" Prentice Hall, New York, (1945)
93. Maslow, Abraham: "Motivation and Personality" Harper & Bros., New York (1954)
94. Brill, A.: "Freud's Contribution to Psychiatry" W. W. Norton & Co., New York 1944)
95. Bowlby, John: "Maternal Care and Mental Health" W.H.O., Geneva (1952)
96. Gesell, Arnold: "Child Development" Harper Brothers, New York (1949)
97. Piaget, Jean: "La Construction du Réèl Chez l'Enfant" Delachant & Niestlé, SA, Paris (1937)

98. Hall, Lindzey: "Theories of Personality" John Wiley & Sons, New York, (1957)
99. Feifel, Herman: "The Meaning of Death" McGraw Hill Book Company, New York (1959)
100. Klineberg: "Social Psychology" Henry Holt, New York (1940)
101. Alexander, Franz: "Psychoanalytic Therapy" The Ronald Press Company, New York (1946)
102. Bühler, Charlotte: "Values in Psychotherapy" Free Press of Glencoe, New York (1962)
103. Grotjahn, Martin: "Psychoanalysis and Family Neurosis" W. W. Norton & Co., New York (1960)
104. Rogers, Carl: "On Becoming a Person" Houghton Mifflin, Boston (1961)
105. Klapper: "The Effects of Mass Communications" The Free Press of Glencoe, New York (1960)
106. Huxley, J.: "Religion without Revelation" Harper Bros., New York (1957)
107. May, Rollo: "Man's Search for Himself" W. W. Norton & Co., (1951)
108. Lippitt, R.: "An Experimental Study of the Effect of Democratic and Authoritarian Group Atmosphere" Univ. Iowa and Stud. I. Childwelfare 16 (1940)
109. Mc Dougall, William: "An Introduction of Social Psychology" Methuen, London (1908)
110. Cooley, C.: "Human Nature and Social Order" Scribner, New York (1902)
111. Gouldner, A.: "Studies in Leadership" Harper Bros., New York (1950)
112. Kardiner, A. & Linton: "The Individual and His Society" Columbia Univ. Press, New York (1939)
113. Moreno, J.: "Who Shall Survive?" Nerv. & Ment. Dis., Washington, D.C. (1934)
114. Goldschmidt, W.: "Exploring the Ways of Mankind" Holt, Rinehart & Winston, New York (1960)
115. Mead, Margaret & Wolfenstein: "Childhood in Contemporary Cultures" Univ. Chicago Press, Chicago (1955)
116. Tillich, Paul: "Religion in a Changing World"

117. Major, Ralph: "A History of Medicine" Springfield, Illinois, (1955)
118. Jastow, M.: "Babylonian-Assyrian Medicine" AMH 19231 (1927)
119. Jones, W.H.S.: "Philosophy and Medicine in Ancient Greece" Baltimore (1946)
120. Petersen, W.F.: "Hippocratic Wisdom" Springfield, Illinois (1946)
121. Riesman: "History of Medicine in the Middle Ages" New York (1935)
122. Pusey, W.A.: "The History of Epidemiology" Springfield, (1933)
123. Saussure, R. de: "French Psychiatry in the Eighteenth Century" CIBA Symposium (1950)
124. Bettman, Otto: "A Pictorial History of Medicine" Charles Thomas, Springfield (1956)
125. Lombroso, C.: "Genie & Irrsinn"
126. Uris, Leon: "Exodus" Doubleday & Co., New York (1958)
127. Lengyel, Olga: "Five Chimneys" Davis Co., New York (1947)
128. Kant, Immanuel: "Critique der Reinen Vernunft" Hartknoch (1781)
129. Schopenhauer: "Philosophie" Jul. Frauenstädt, Leipzig

INDEX

A

Abraham, 42, 50
abstract thinking, 31
Adam and Eve, 118
addiction to surgery, 110
Adler, Alfred, 83, 184
adolescence, 179-180
adoption, 149-150
African customs, 47, 51
Agamemnon, 43
Agatha, Holy, 51
aggression, 9, 13, 14, 27, 115
Ajase complex, 153
alcoholics, 29
Algolagnie, 28
American Constitution, 88
Anaclitic Depression, 28
anal sadomasochist, 125
anal stage of development,
    30, 124-125, 129
ancient history, 120-121
anesthesia, 54
animal behaviour, 8, 17-18
animals, cruelty to, 19-20
animals, intercourse with,
    20-21
anthropologists, 31
Aphrodisiacum, 19
arrest, 85-86, 88
arson, 62
Art, 23, 24, 144
ascesis, 45, 48
ascetics, 47, 55
atheists, 54
Augustine, St., 49

B

Babylonian medical customs,
    106
barbershops, 31
barbersurgeons, 104
bath, 103
Battered Child Syndrome,
    10, 165-171, 177
beauty parlours, 31
beggars, 12
B'hai, 58
blind, 12, 185
blood-letting, 114-115
Boccaccio, 24, 54
body-build, 37
bond service, 70
Brahmin, 45, 46, 52
Braille, Louis, 184
Buddha, 47
Buddhist, 45, 48
bullfights, 18, 19
burial customs, 15

C

Cain, 168
Calligula, 9, 121
capital punishment, 73-75
career, choice of, 111, 113,
    115, 132-133, 143.
case histories:
    animal tormentor Regi-
        nald, 175
    Australian girl, 95-96
    Barbie murderous impulses,
        30

201

Q

Quasimodo, 24

R

rage reaction, 29
religion, 41, 63
religion, susceptibility of children to, 169
rights of the mentally ill, 97
Roman Law, 49
Romans, 17
rope torture, 72
Rousseau, 20, 23, 165.
Russian torture instruments, 70

S

Sacher-Masoch, 22, 23
sacrifice, 41-42, 51, 57, 111
Sade, Marquis de, 22, 37, 123-124
sadism, 14, 22, 27, 28, 38, 50, 54, 81, 115
sadism towards cripples, 150, 184
sadomasochism, 14, 178-179
sadomasochism in
    dentistry, 104-106
    drug-addiction, 116
    hypnosis, 115
    nursing, 129
    medicine, 112-117
      medieval, 103
    research, 107-108
    surgery, 106, 109-112
Salk, 18
Salomé, 24
Salpétrière, 102
scapegoat, 39, 55, 76, 93, 94
schools, 147, 182-184
Schopenhauer, 11

science versus religion, 8
schizophrenics 51
self-castration, 110
self-destruction, 14, 189
self-experimentation, 116
self-mutilation, 25, 28, 44, 51, 55
self-punishment, 28
self-torture, 28, 47
sensuality among the Romans, 17-18
Sermon on the Mount, 51
sex, 17
sex-drive, 23
sexology, 22
sexual customs, 21
Shakespeare, 23, 37, 183
shock treatment, 104
sibling rivalry, 175
silicosis, 119
Skoptsi, 57-61, 62-63
slang, 180
slaughter methods, 19
slavery, 12, 67-69, 78-79
social versus individual hatred, 76
sociogenetic evolution, 39
Socrates, 49
South Slavonian customs, 21
Spartacus, 74
sperm choler, 89
spiders, 17
State's responsibility, 16
Stekel, 27
step-parents, 169-171
student revolt, reason for, 180
sublimated drives, 113
suicide 29, 46, 48-49, 50, 61, 178
superego, 12

Superman, 11
surgeons, 111
surgeons' callousness, 110
surgery for punishment, 106
symbols, 31-32

T

Tapasvinas, 48
Tarantism, 44
Tarde, 118
Tattoo, 91
teachers, 182-183
television, 25
Termagant, Lady Flaybum, 144
thalidomide, 108
Thanatos, 27
Thérèse et Isabelle, 159
Tiberius 9, 15, 120-121
tonsure, 31
torture, 54, 73-74, 90
torture instruments, 72-73
torture in hospitals, 102, 103-104
transvestitism, 34-36
Tropic Choler, 68, 89

tropical climates, 47
tymbals, 64

U

underprivileged children, 83
uniform standards, 119

V

Van Gogh, 51
vegetarians, 20
violence, 10
voluntary hospitalization, 110

W

war, 16, 89, 157-158, 189
water torture, 72
Wertheim, Frederic, 25
whipping, 56
Wilde, Oscar, 24
witchcraft, 52
witches, 53-54

Y

Yogis, 47

Z

Zola, 24